▶▶▶▶ hairflair ◀◀◀◀

easy steps to great new looks

INDEX

This edition published by Index
Index House
Unit 1
A1-M1 Centre
Garrard Way
Kettering
Northants NN16 8TD

ISBN: 1-85605-344-X

Material previously published as part of the
encyclopedia set *The New You* (Orbis Publishing).

The publisher cannot be held responsible for any loss, injury or
damage caused as a result of the techniques described in this book.

Editorial and design: Brown Packaging Ltd,
255-257 Liverpool Road, London N1 1LX

Printed in the Slovak Republic

CONTENTS

• TECHNIQUE 1 •
BUILDING VOLUME

BEFORE

Building body into your hair is the perfect starting point for many styles – whether you're blow-drying a smooth bob, scrunch-drying curls, or dressing long hair – which is why it's the first technique covered in HAIR STYLING. It makes hair appear thicker and gives it a bouncy quality. Try this technique and then read on for this week's project: how to make your hair curl with bendy rollers.

PREPARATION

TIME	HAVE TO HAND
30 minutes, depending on hair length	• towel • styling mousse • wide-toothed comb • hairdryer • butterfly clips or hair grips • hairbrush • tail-comb • hairspray

1 ▶ ▶ ▶ ▶ ▶ ▶ ▶ ▶ ▶ ▶
Wash and blot-dry your hair. Spread a golf-ball sized blob of styling mousse between your hands and smooth it evenly over your hair. Use your fingertips to work it well into the root area, and a wide-toothed comb to carry it down to the hair ends.

1

HAIR STYLING

2
Using a cool dryer, rough-dry your hair to remove excess water. Turn your head upside-down and use your fingers to lift your hair away from the scalp to create more volume.

3
For maximum root lift, blow-dry the lower layers of your hair, brushing them outwards, almost horizontally to the scalp. Follow the brush along the hair length with your hairdryer, turning the ends under the brush.

tip Use your fingers as a guide to the correct temperature for drying: if it's too hot for your fingers, it's too hot for your hair.

4
Continue lifting the hair with a brush as you dry the top lengths. When the roots are completely dry, create still more volume on top by 'hooking' the brush into the hair near the roots, lifting it up and blowing air through.

tip Dry root area completely before back-combing, as any dampness will cause volume and root-lift to collapse.

PROBLEM
•SOLVER•

SECTIONING

If you have a problem keeping your hair away from the area you're working on, try sectioning. Professional hairdressers use it to limit the amount of hair around the brush while blow-drying, giving better control and neater results.

Use a comb to divide the back of your hair to about half-way down into a neat, vertical parting. Secure the two parted sections on top of the head with butterfly clips, leaving the lower section loose. The front section can also be left free. Thicker or longer hair can be twisted or coiled before clipping.

When styling long hair, use your comb to divide the lower lengths of hair into manageable sections by separating the back from the sides.

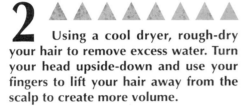

5
Back-comb the under-layers of your hair to create extra volume. Hold small sections of hair at right angles to your head. Place your comb 2.5cm (1in) away from your scalp and gently tease the hair down towards the roots. Back-comb the hair length every 2.5 cm (1in), leaving the last 5cm (2in) free from back-combing.

6
Use your fingers or a brush to smooth your hair into style. To help it stay in place, spray the hair lightly and evenly with hairspray. Don't spray too close or too heavily as the hair will become damp.

tip For a looser, more natural style, apply hairspray directly to your hairbrush and run it lightly through your hair.

HAIR STYLING TECHNIQUE 1: BUILDING VOLUME

HOW HAIR GROWS

● There are somewhere between 90,000 and 150,000 hair follicles in the scalp.
● Each hair follicle has a sebaceous (or oil) gland sac that lubricates the hair.
● The papilla of blood vessels at the base of each follicle feeds nutrients to the hair cells.
● The hair cells harden and die, and are pushed through a narrow tunnel and out through the scalp.
● The hair that comes out of the scalp is already dead, though it continues to lengthen as more cells multiply within the follicle.

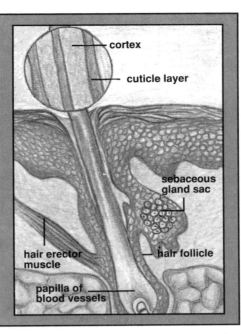

cortex

cuticle layer

sebaceous gland sac

hair follicle

hair erector muscle

papilla of blood vessels

TRICKS
of the trade

USING A DIFFUSER

● *A diffuser slots on to the end of a hairdryer nozzle, dispersing the air. You place handfuls of hair inside the diffuser as you dry. Diffusing dries hair gently to give it more body and curl, while reducing the risk of heat damage.*
● *It boosts curl on naturally wavy and permed hair. It also gives body to long straight hair. It takes longer to dry hair with a diffuser but the results are better.*

Suit yourself

Build volume into any hair length by adapting the basic technique.

CURLY HAIR
● Apply mousse to your hair.
● Tilt your head to one side and lift the hair roots away from the scalp.
● Scrunch-dry each section of hair by screwing it into a tight ball.
● Finger-comb the hair to separate the curls and give extra definition.

LONG HAIR
● Apply styling spray directly to the roots of damp hair (a stronger hold spray is needed for long hair).

SHORT HAIR
● Spread a coin-sized blob of firm-hold gel between your hands and work it through towel-dried hair. Pay special attention to the roots.
● Blow-dry, using your fingers to grip the hair and lift it upwards from the scalp.
● When the hair is completely dry, smooth the surface lightly with your fingers or a brush.
● Mist with hairspray.

● If you have a diffuser, attach it to your hairdryer when blow-drying your hair to prevent the curls from being 'blown away'. Use the hairdryer on a cool setting.

● Tip your head upside-down and direct the hairdryer upwards into the hair. Dry the roots thoroughly, otherwise all the root-lift will be lost. Use your fingertips to judge: if your hair feels cold, it is still damp.

• PROJECT 1 • BENDY ROLLERS

Once you've learnt how to add volume, you can experiment with other styles that give even more bounce. Try our first project and discover how to use bendy rollers to create soft waves, spirals or ringlets.

PREPARATION

TIME
about 60 minutes (including 30 minutes drying time)

HAVE TO HAND
• hair grips or butterfly clips • styling spray • 20 flexible foam rollers (the more you use, the greater the volume you create).

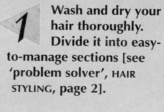

BEFORE

1 Wash and dry your hair thoroughly. Divide it into easy-to-manage sections [see 'problem solver', HAIR STYLING, page 2].

tip *Save time when setting long hair in bendy rollers by tying hair back in a ponytail first. Free one small section of hair for curling at a time, using a tail-comb.*

2 Starting with the underlayers, take a section at a time and sub-divide the hair into smaller sections. For medium-sized curls, make 3-5cm (1.5-2in) sections; for tighter curls, divide the hair into thinner sections. Coat each section with styling spray, using enough to cover the hair, but not enough to make it wet.

4

3 Wind each small section tightly around the centre of the foam roller, keeping the same tension for each strand. Wind the roller right up to the hair roots, allowing the hair to spread naturally over the roller.

4 Bring the ends of each roller together until they overlap. Bend them in the opposite direction to the way you wound the hair. Secure the rollers firmly on the lower sections of hair, as they support the rollers on top.

Did you know...?

- On average, each follicle produces 0.33mm of hair per day, 12 cm in a whole year, and an astounding 7.6 metres during a lifetime!
- Normal hair loss is between 30 and 120 hairs per day. Each hair grows only about 80cm before the new hair underneath begins to grow and to push it out of the follicle.
- Normal hair loss stops during pregnancy, making the woman's hair particularly thick and luxuriant at this time.

5 To give the top lengths a more natural, S-shaped curl, twist the sections before winding. Make sure they are all twisted in the same direction. Spray with styling spray and wind each section around the bendy rollers. Now leave your hair to set for 30 minutes.

TRICKS — of the trade

winding towards the back of your head.
- *For spiral curls, twist each top section of hair around your finger, before winding the hair around the rollers.*
- *To create waves on the lower layers, wind each section tightly but evenly around the centre of the bendy roller and allow the hair to spread across its length.*

6 Remove the rollers and use your fingers to loosen the curls and style your hair. Turn your head upside-down and lift the hair to add volume.

tip To help the curls last, try misting your hair with hairspray after removing the rollers. Allow the hair to dry before finger-combing it through.

WINDING HAIR

- *Wind hair sections in alternating forward and backward directions for a natural wavy effect.*
- *When curling the front sections, style the hair away from your face by*

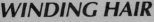
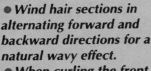

SPIRAL   WAVES

HAIR STYLING PROJECT 1: BENDY ROLLERS

Suit yourself

★ While certain bendy rollers give fabulous results on some hair lengths and types, others don't work so well. Follow our tips and recommendations to help you find the bendy rollers that will give the best results for your hair.

The width of the bendy roller doesn't necessarily affect the size of the curl. This is determined by the amount of hair you wrap round each roller.

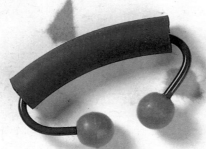

Short rubber rollers
Hair length: short to shoulder length.
Tip: for tighter curls, divide the hair into small 1cm (0.5in) sections and use extra rollers. If you have short, fine, tangle-free hair, try curling your hair with pipe cleaners – a cheap alternative to bendy rollers.

Wide rubber rollers
Hair length or type: long, thick, curly or frizzy.
Tip: use more than 20 bendy rollers for the best results. Use 5-8cm (2-3in) sections of hair.

Thin foam rollers
Hair length: short layers.
Narrow bendy rollers are suitable for short top layers or a fringe. They grip short hair better than wide foam rollers.
Tip: Wrap tissue round the bottom of uneven hair ends to hold them in place as you turn the hair round the rollers.

Fabric rollers
Hair length or type: dry, damaged or layered.
Good for damaged or layered hair as it is trapped between the two halves of the fabric roller. Fabric rollers are available in different widths.
Tip: fabric rollers are soft and lightweight, so you can sleep in them overnight for longer-lasting results.

Heated bendy rollers
Hair length: shoulder length.
Tip: make sure hair is clean and dry before you begin. The secret to success lies in wrapping small amounts of hair round the roller and gently teasing your hair out at the end.
Advantage: more durable than foam rollers. They are more effective than unheated rollers. Use on dry hair and then wait for the rollers to cool down before carefully taking them out.
Disadvantage: they are about five times as expensive as heated bendy rollers.

Twist 'n' curl rollers
Hair length:
Tip: the kit comes with styling spray. For best results, be sparing with the spray. Wash spray out the next day as although it adds lots of volume it can leave hair feeling lank and heavy.
Advantage: lightweight and easy to handle.

6

• TECHNIQUE 2 •
USING GEL

Like hairspray, hair gel is a setting agent and is designed to make your hairstyle last longer. It is especially useful for sculpting, taming and adding texture to sleek, short styles. In technique 2, we show you how to apply gel for best results.

BEFORE

BEFORE

PREPARATION

TIME	HAVE TO HAND
10-15 minutes	• hair gel • fine-toothed comb • hairdryer • brush

TRICKS — *of the trade*

• *Too much gel can leave hair feeling stiff, so use it sparingly.*
• *Try spreading gel on your hair before applying rollers as a substitute for old-fashioned setting lotion.*
• *Use gel before plaiting to add extra control and a sleek finish to your hair.*

1 ▶ ▶ ▶ ▶ ▶ ▶ ▶ ▶ ▶ ▶ ▶
Spread a coin-sized dollop of gel between your hands and work into clean, towel-dried hair. Use your fingertips to rub it well into the roots, then comb through to distribute the gel evenly through to the hair ends.

⭐ *tip* *Gels are easy to use, but don't use too much. The secret is to start with a small amount, you can always apply more if necessary.*

7

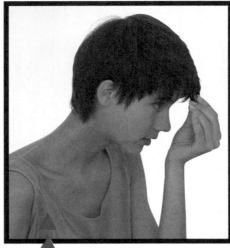

Gels are made from a thick water-based liquid, rather like old-fashioned setting lotion. They are available in different strengths and have a number of properties. For example, wet-look gels contain a high oil content to add shine.

Firm hold – adds staying power to your hairstyle.
Extra hold – adds extra staying power for difficult hair.
Strong hold – usually the strongest level of hold. For styles that are extremely difficult to manage.
Mega hold – not available in all styling ranges. This offers maximum holding power for styles that defy gravity.
Wet-look – adds a shiny appearance to hair and provides extra hold.
Spray gel – the spray offers precision application for detailed styling. It's thinner and less messy than ordinary gel.
Volumising gel – builds volume and root-lift into hair.

2 ▲▲▲▲▲▲▲ Begin blow-drying the front section of hair. Use a hairbrush to lift hair away from your forehead to encourage root-lift and body. Use the same lifting technique to blow-dry the top lengths. The sides and back can be blow-dried smooth.

 tip *Comb the hair you're not drying out of the way and work on one section of hair at a time.*

3 ▲▲▲▲▲▲▲ Rub a little extra gel between your finger and thumb and pull side wisps forwards on to the face. Finish off the look by separating your fringe into spikes.

tip *Try using wet-look gel to add a touch of gloss. Dry hair will look less dull and lifeless if wet-look gel is applied sparingly at the crown.*

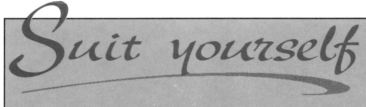

Suit yourself

An at-a-glance guide to finding the right gel for your hair type and length.

DRY HAIR
• Use wet-look gel.
Add a touch of gloss by smoothing a little wet-look gel over a few chosen strands of hair at the crown. Some gels contain a sun-screen, which helps protect hair from the drying effects of the sun.

LANK HAIR
• Use strong-hold gel.
For maximum lift and volume, apply strong-hold gel to the roots only. Use your fingers to lift the hair away from the scalp as you blow-dry.

STRAIGHT HAIR
• Use normal-hold gel.
For a wavy effect, apply gel sparingly to your hair and comb it through into a wave. Clip in position and dry.

WAVY HAIR
• Use normal-hold gel.
To smooth and straighten wavy hair, apply gel and blow-dry your hair, smoothing over gently with a hairbrush.

CURLY HAIR
• Use normal-hold gel.
Spread a small amount of normal-hold gel between your hands and slide your fingers through the ends to give curls a crisp texture and greater definition.

MEDIUM-LENGTH BOB
• Use volumising gel.
Comb gel through from the crown to the ends. Tilt your head forwards as you blow-dry to add lift.

LONG HAIR
• Use spray gel.
Spray damp hair with gel, paying particular attention to the roots. Tilt your head forwards and blow-dry your hair for extra volume and body. Lightly spray your hair with more gel when dry.

FINE HAIR
• Use volumising gel.
Rub gel into small sections of hair close to the roots. As you rub, separate the strands to give a fuller look to the hair. Volume-building gel will make fine hair appear thicker.

HAIR STYLING TECHNIQUE 2: USING GEL

THREE WAYS WITH GEL

Discover the versatility of gel. Use it to create sophisticated, slicked back styles for day and evening or to ruffle your hair for a softer look.

1 CITY STYLE

1 Squeeze gel along the teeth of a fine-toothed comb. Comb the gel through the hair at the crown first, so that most of the gel is over the top lengths, for maximum styling support.

⭐ **tip** *Keep hair damp so that the gel remains soft, pliable and spreads through the hair more easily. Once gel is dry, it solidifies and is difficult to work with.*

2 Use your fingers to style your hair as you dry. Lift the top hair lengths up and back from the crown. In a similar way, style the front sections of your hair back off your face.

⭐ **tip** *Pay particular attention to drying the roots. Damp hair will cause root-lift to collapse. If the root area feels cool to touch, it is still damp.*

3 Use a fine-toothed comb to smooth the sides of your hair down towards the nape of your neck. Add a little extra gel to the comb to smooth down stray ends.

⭐ **tip** *Take care not to overwork the hair or the gel will dry out and crack, causing the hair to lose its shape. Don't attempt to shape your hair once the gel has dried as it will simply brush out.*

9

2 SLICKED BACK

1 Mist clean dry hair with water to dampen it. Then, using your fingers, work wet-look gel into your hair. Scrunch handfuls of hair in the palm of your hand to add movement.

tip *When restyling, avoid using too much gel as it can make your hair look dull and stringy. If you overdo the gel, wash your hair and start again.*

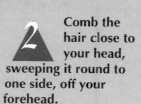

2 Comb the hair close to your head, sweeping it round to one side, off your forehead.

WATCHPOINTS

- Some gels can dry into flakes on the surface of your scalp and resemble dandruff. Others can dry out the hair if used too frequently. To avoid these conditions, use alcohol-free gel, and try using rich hair conditioners when you wash your hair.
- Regular gel users will have to wash their hair more frequently, as a build-up of gel can make hair sticky and harder to style.
- Gel can make 'relaxed' afro hair become frizzy.

Did you know...?

- All styling aids that are applied to hair are based on the same ingredient – a plastic-type resin that stiffens as it dries. However, gel, mousse and hairspray are all suspended in different substances.

3 TOUSLED LOOK

1 To restyle dry hair, use spray gel. Alternatively, reactivate existing gel by softening it with a little water.

tip *Use a fine plant spray filled with water to dampen your hair. Take care not to make your hair too wet as this will dilute the gel, making it less effective.*

2 Ruffle the top sections and pull the hair towards your forehead for a casual, tousled look. Finger-comb the sides forward too, so that they frame the face and draw attention to your eyes.

tip *Give a wispy effect to the hair ends by rubbing them firmly between finger and thumb.*

HAIR STYLING PROJECT 2: THREE WAYS WITH GEL

BEFORE

PREPARATION

TIME *5–10 minutes, depending on hair length*

HAVE TO HAND
● comb ● covered hair bands ● hair accessories (like stretchy fabric hair twists) ● grips or pins ● hair wax or gel (optional)

• TECHNIQUE 3 •

PLAITING

Plaiting is a simple technique of which there are many styling variations. It is an excellent way of controlling curly hair or putting waves in straight hair. All you really need is hair that is at least chin length and elasticated hair bands to secure the ends.

1 Part your hair half-way between a centre parting and the top of your ear. Separate the lower section into three neat and equal strands, and begin plaiting by crossing the front strand over the middle strand. Holding what was the original middle strand at the front, cross the back section of hair over the new middle strand.

 tip
Keep the rest of your hair brushed out of the way or tie it back with a covered elastic band.

11

2 ▲▲▲▲▲▲▲▲ Keeping the tension tight and even so that the plait doesn't become irregular, cross the front strand over the middle strand once more to finish the first 'V' of your plait. The original front and back strands have now swapped places.

⭐ *tip* *It's better not to plait using a mirror as the reversed image can be confusing. Try to rely on your sense of touch.*

3 ▲▲▲▲▲▲▲ Continue the front-over-middle, back-over-middle weaving technique down to about 2.5cm (1in) from the ends. Secure the plait with a covered elastic hair band.

⭐ *tip* *If the finished plait is too fine to secure easily with a covered elastic band, tie it tightly with string. This grips well and will not tear the hair.*

4 ▲▲▲▲▲ Make a second plait by braiding the section of hair between the first plait and a centre parting. Using the same technique, make two plaits on the other side of your face.

⭐ *tip* *Dampen your hair with water to keep the hair sections smooth and separate. This makes plaiting easier and creates a neater result.*

5 ▲▲▲▲▲▲▲ Pull all four strands to the back of your head and secure them where they meet. Place a second fabric band over the elastic hair band or string.

⭐ *tip* *Choose fabric hair twists or hair slides in different colours or patterns for added interest. Don't ever use uncovered elastic bands as this can damage the hair cuticle.*

Suit yourself
an at-a-glance guide to how to plait any hair length

CHIN-LENGTH HAIR
Apply gel to damp hair to keep shorter top lengths flat and under control. French plait the top section of hair for about 5cm (2in). Secure with a covered elastic band or tuck the ends under the plait and secure in position with hair grips.

SHOULDER-LENGTH BLUNT-CUT BOB
Secure your hair into a high ponytail at the crown.

Divide the hair into four equal sections. Plait one section and carefully wind it round the base of your ponytail.

Tuck the ends underneath and fasten securely with a hair clip, leaving the tail loose.

MID-LENGTH LAYERED BOB
French plait the top half of your hair down as far as your ears.

Stop adding extra hair and plait down to the ends, then fasten, leaving the rest of your hair loose.

SHORT HAIR
You can even wear plaits if you have short hair with the help of hair extensions. First take a 2.5cm (1in) section of hair from behind your ears and plait it to the ends.

Attach the plait extension by pulling the end of your own plait through the loop at the top of the false plait.

Secure it by winding a length of wool from your roots to 5cm (2.5cm) below the join.

HAIR STYLING TECHNIQUE 3: PLAITING

BEFORE

· PROJECT 3 ·
FRENCH PLAIT

Once you've got into the swing of basic plaiting, try the French plait. There are endless variations of this technique and you'll be surprised at how easy it is to achieve a look that is both stylish and manageable.

PREPARATION

TIME *5–10 minutes*

HAVE TO HAND
● comb ● covered hair band ● hair pins ● hair wax or gel (optional)

1 Use your thumbs to scoop up side sections of hair from above the ears and join them at the crown. Separate this tail into three equal strands. Begin by using the basic plaiting technique, crossing the left strand over the middle one.

tip *Include your fringe into the plait by weaving from the top of your head.*

2 Continue the basic plait by crossing the right strand over the middle section.

tip *Beginners may find it easier to begin plaiting from further down the back of the head. This also looks less severe.*

13

3 ▶ Pick up extra hair from one side, join it to the nearest section and continue plaiting, crossing it over the centre strand. (This new section of hair should be approximately half as thick as the original strand.) Repeat on the other side and carry on joining and plaiting until you reach the nape of the neck.

4 ▶ When there is no new hair left to add, continue basic plaiting until you reach the ends of the hair. Secure your French plait with a covered elastic band. For a more formal variation, try tucking the plait under itself at the nape of the neck and securing it with grips or pins.

PLAITING VARIATIONS

Look special for an evening out or simply business-like by trying these intricate plaits.

LOOP ▶ ▶

Part your hair in the centre and French plait each side of the head separately. When you reach the nape of your neck, secure each plait temporarily with a covered elastic hair band.

Roll the plaits over each other and secure them together with pins or grips for a chic evening look.

◀ SPIRAL ▶

To create this spiral, French plait your hair anti-clockwise, beginning at the crown. The braid should pass over each ear, across the top of your fringe (which can be woven in or left out), and down to the nape of the neck. Plait the end-lengths together and secure.

This plait looks equally elegant wound into a coil and secured with a hair grip.

HAIR STYLING PROJECT 3: FRENCH PLAIT

• TECHNIQUE 4 •

IN-BETWEEN HAIR LENGTHS

Growing out a fringe or layers requires a lot of patience, but don't despair, our styling ideas for short and long hair are the answer to your frustration.

TIME *5-10 minutes*

HAVE TO HAND
• round brush • vent brush • hair mousse • sculpting lotion

SHORT HAIR: THE WILD LOOK

SHORT HAIR: GROWING OUT A FRINGE

LONG HAIR: GROWING OUT LAYERS

LONG HAIR: THE EVENING LOOK

15

1 SHORT HAIR: THE WILD LOOK

BEFORE

1 ▲▲▲▲▲▲▲
Wash and towel-dry your hair and then blow-dry it using a round styling brush to add lift.

2 ▲▲▲▲▲▲▲▲▲
Using a fine-toothed comb, back-comb small sections of hair every 2.5cm (1in) down the hair length. Work systematically from the front to the back of your head.

⭐ **tip** *If you're in a hurry, you can back-comb your hair without washing and blow-drying it first. Simply brush your hair with a vent brush to separate out the strands before you start.*

3 ▲▲▲▲▲▲▲▲
Using an Afro comb, pick out individual hair strands to give extra definition to the finished style. Use the comb to create a tousled effect or to lift flat spots.

⭐ **tip** *To define the curls, warm a little wax between your fingers and rub it into the individual hair strands. Spray mist your hair with hairspray to keep the style in place all evening.*

TRICKS of the trade

SPLIT ENDS
● *When you are growing out short layers, make sure you have your hair trimmed regularly. Any hairstyle will become unmanageable if the ends become split or straggly. Try to have your hair trimmed every six to eight weeks.*

HAIR STYLING TECHNIQUE 4: IN-BETWEEN HAIR LENGTHS

2 SHORT HAIR: GROWING OUT A FRINGE

1 Wash and towel-dry your hair. Switch the hairdryer to a cool setting and blow-dry the front and side sections. Use a round styling brush to sweep your hair back off your forehead. Keep the hairdryer at least 15cm (6in) away from your hair strands as you dry.

★ *tip* *Apply a small blob of mousse to your damp fringe before you start drying to hold the finished style.*

Did you know...?

• Hair doesn't grow at the same rate – which is why styles lose their shape.
• Hair grows fastest between the ages of 15-30, and slows down after 50.
• Hair grows faster in the summer than in the winter.
• Hair has elastic properties enabling it to stretch to between one-fifth and one-third of its original length. Wet hair is more elastic than dry hair, while heat increases the elasticity of hair.

2 When your hair is completely dry, brush it through using a vent brush. This gives your hair a groomed yet textured finish.

★ *tip* *A vent brush is good for styling your hair as you blow-dry. The vents allow hot air to pass through the brush for better control when styling, without stretching the hair strands.*

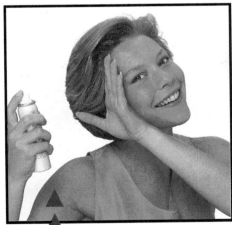

3 Shielding your eyes with your hand, lightly spray your fringe with hairspray from a distance of 15-25cm (6-10in). The hairspray holds your fringe in place and stops it flopping forwards into your eyes.

★ *tip* *If your hair is very fine or determined to flop forwards, use strong-hold hairspray or hair gel.*

17

HAIR STYLING TECHNIQUE 4: IN-BETWEEN HAIR LENGTHS

HAIR STYLING

3 LONG HAIR: GROWING OUT LAYERS

BEFORE

1 Spray sculpting lotion on to clean, towel-dried hair. Concentrate the lotion on the top lengths, then comb it through the hair to distribute it evenly.

⭐ *tip* Pump-action spray setting lotions offer precise application, allowing you to direct the styling spray exactly where it is needed.

2 Switch your hairdryer to a cool setting and rough dry your hair. Keep the dryer moving all the time and tip your head forwards so you can build volume into the hair roots.

⭐ *tip* If your hair has a natural wave, scrunch up handfuls of hair in the palm of your hand as you blow-dry to boost the curl and volume.

3 Gather up all your shorter hair lengths at the crown. Twist them together, and then push the hair forwards so that the front forms a soft, rolled effect. Secure the twist behind the 'roll' with hair grips.

⭐ *tip* Separating the shorter top layers of hair will make the rest of the hair appear uniform in length.

18

HAIR STYLING TECHNIQUE 4: IN-BETWEEN HAIR LENGTHS

4 LONG HAIR: EVENING LOOK

TRICKS of the trade

HAIR ACCESSORIES
● *Make the most of accessories when you're growing out your layers. If you have short hair, try tying your hair up with a 50s-style scarf. If you have longer hair, pull back your fringe or hide short top layers under a thick fabric hair band. If you are trying to grow out your fringe, brush it forwards and then sweep it up and over to one side. Hold your hair off your face with a decorative hair comb to give a soft, rolled effect.*

1 To add body and curl to straight long hair, use heated rollers. Divide your hair into sections, then roll each section in a heated roller and secure with hair pins. Wait until the rollers have cooled down and take them out.

 tip *If your hair takes the curl very easily, take the rollers out before they are cool to prevent your hair from becoming too curly. Gently loosen the curls into waves with your fingertips.*

2 When you have removed the rollers, turn your head upside-down and shake your head to loosen the hair at the roots. Separate individual curls with your fingers. Do not comb or brush your hair because you will lose the waves.

tip *For a tousled, romantic style, stop at this point and lightly spray the individual curls with hairspray to hold the style in place all evening.*

3 Gather together your hair ends in a loose tail at the nape of the neck and twist them together. Lift the tail up the back of the neck and make a pleat by tucking in the tail against your head. Secure it in place with hair pins. Allow the top layers of hair to fall naturally. Use your fingers to sculpt your fringe, if you have one.

 tip *Pull out a few hair strands at the back and the sides to soften the style.*

19

HAIR STYLING TECHNIQUE 4: IN-BETWEEN HAIR LENGTHS

• PROJECT 4 •

TRIMMING YOUR FRINGE

Do you find that your fringe grows at an uneven rate or needs trimming before the rest of your hair? Rather than having to pay for frequent and costly trips to the hairdresser, try re-shaping or trimming your fringe like a professional at home.

BEFORE

PREPARATION

TIME *20 minutes*

HAVE TO HAND – • fine-toothed comb • hairdressing scissors (available at good chemists)

1 Comb your fringe forwards into a clean workable line. Divide your fringe in half with a horizontal parting and clip back the top section before you start trimming. To help you cut in a straight line, support your cutting hand.

tip *Always cut your fringe dry. Wet hair stretches and rises up when dry.*

2 Release your hair clip and comb down the top section of your fringe. Using the trimmed lower layer as your guide, cut the top layer to the same length, supporting your cutting hand all the way across your forehead.

tip *Trim your fringe using a series of short snips. Cut the edges of your fringe straight, don't shape them.*

3 Check that your fringe is even by pulling the hair strands taut as you run your fingers down the strands. Lastly, dampen down your fringe and blow-dry, curling the ends under with a styling brush.

tip *Curling the hair ends under gives a soft, natural finish.*

20

BEFORE

Ponytails are one of the quickest ways of taking your hair off your face. There are lots of variations to try for long, medium-length and short hair, and ponytails can look sporty or smart depending on how they're worn and on your choice of hair accessories.

• TECHNIQUE 5 •
PONYTAILS

PREPARATION

TIME 5 minutes

HAVE TO HAND
• hairbrush • covered elastic band •
hair accessories • **heated rollers** •
curling tongs

1 Tilt your head forwards and brush your hair over from the back of your head down to the ends. This removes any tangles and makes your hair easier to tie back in a smooth ponytail.

⭐ *tip* *Brushing also helps add shine by encouraging the cuticle scales to lie flat so that they reflect the light.*

2 Gather your hair together at the back of your crown with one hand, and secure it in place with a covered elastic band. Do not pull the hair too tight, and loosen the tension at the hairline with your fingers.

⭐ *tip* *Never use plain elastic bands as these can cause split ends and damage the overall condition of the hair.*

3 For decoration, tie a pretty fabric hair twist or a ribbon on top of the covered elastic band. Choose a band in a fabric to match or contrast with your clothes.

⭐ *tip* *You can just use a fabric hair twist to hold your ponytail, but avoid silky fabrics as these won't grip your hair quite as well.*

21

• PROJECT 5 •

5 WAYS WITH PONYTAILS

BRAIDED PONYTAIL

1 Tie your hair back with a covered elastic band, and smooth down any short wisps or stray ends with wax or wet-look gel. When applying wax, rub a dot of it between your fingers to warm it and then run the palms of your hands over your hair.

★ **tip** *The oil in the wax conditions the hair, adds gloss and provides extra hold. To prevent your hair looking greasy, use wax sparingly.*

2 Pin one end of a length of gold braid or ribbon to your elastic band with a hair grip. Wind the braid round the band and down the tail itself in a spiral. When you reach the last 5cm (2in) section of your hair, where your ponytail begins to thin out, stop binding your hair.

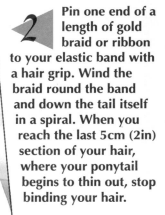

★ **tip** *To help you see what you're doing, look in a mirror and hold your ponytail above your head.*

3 Keeping the tension even, wind the braid back up towards the crown, and tuck the free end of the braid under the elastic band.

★ **tip** *If necessary, secure the free end of the braid with a hair grip. Fasten the braid under the ponytail and tuck in the hair grip.*

22

TOP KNOT

1 Tilt your head forwards and brush all your hair into a ponytail. Make sure your ponytail is centred and then secure it with a covered elastic band.

tip Use gel or hairspray to hold any shorter lower layers up at the back. If your layers are too short, let them hang down in soft wisps.

2 Neatly divide your ponytail into five separate sections. Set each section in a heated roller by winding the roller in towards your scalp. Pin each heated roller in place and leave to cool.

tip Use fewer rollers on thin or fine hair; more on very thick hair. Bendy foam rollers can be used instead.

3 Gently release your hair from the heated rollers without losing the shape of the curls. Loop the curled hair ends up towards the crown and pin them with hair grips to the base of your ponytail.

tip If you have short hair, just divide your hair into sections and curl with heated rollers. Fasten the curls in place with hair grips.

Did you know....?

• You shouldn't wear your ponytail too tight. Prolonged pulling can cause a form of hair loss called *traction alopecia*, which usually occurs at the hair line where hair is under the greatest tension. The condition is usually temporary, unless the hair has been put under strain for many years.
• To prevent hair grips slipping out of freshly washed hair, lightly cover each hair grip with hairspray. If you have fine hair, choose grips that meet at the open end and have bumpy sides.

23

TOUSLED TOP TAIL

1 Gather your hair up in a high ponytail and tie it with an elastic band. Take 2.5cm (1in) sections of hair and curl them with heated curling tongs. Curl the whole tail length, taking care not to overheat the hair.

tip Before tonging, spray your hair with styling lotion to protect it. Tong each strand for about 30 seconds before releasing the curl.

2 Allow your hair to cool, then break up the curls with your fingers. Do not comb the curls or they will drop out. Lightly mist your curls with hairspray to hold them in place.

tip If your hair is very fine, a little back-combing will help add volume to your ponytail.

Curling tongs

Like electric rollers, curling tongs use heat to realign the molecules of your hair and to give the desired shape.

● Use curling tongs on dry hair. Steam curling tongs are slightly gentler on the hair as the mist of steam adds moisture and this prevents the hair drying out.

● Don't press your hair between the curling tongs for too long.

● Never let hot tongs touch your scalp as they can blister

and damage the skin tissue.

● To use curling tongs: Clamp the end of a 5cm (2in) section of hair on to the styling rod. Gently roll the hair away from your face, stopping before you get to the scalp. Hold for a few seconds, then release the clip and carefully slide the wand out of the curl. Fasten the curl in place until cool.

● Do not use curling tongs to straighten hair. Constant pulling causes breakage.

3 To disguise any shorter strands, lift up your ponytail and wind braid or ribbon around the base to form a band 2.5cm (1in) thick.

tip Brightly coloured towelling bands also look attractive and are good for hiding shorter hair strands.

24

SIXTIES PONYTAIL

1 Start by back-combing the top section of hair, paying particular attention to adding height at the crown. Brush your hair into a centre or side parting, or back off your face.

tip *After back-combing, handle your hair lightly or the extra volume will be lost.*

2 Use a brush and your hand to smooth down your hair ends but leave height and volume at the crown.

tip *If you have just washed your hair, brushing may cause static. Smooth down flyaway strands with wax or hairspray.*

3 Gently pull your hair into a tail at the nape of the neck, and fasten with a hair clip or bow. Smooth down the front section with a hair band.

tip *If you flatten down the hair at the front, the hair at the crown appears higher, and has a more sixties feel.*

WATCHPOINTS

To minimise the damage caused by brushing:
- Avoid using bristle brushes whenever possible. If necessary, use them for styling purposes only, *never* grooming. Bristles leave little room for hair to pass through the brush – when the hair is pulled and stretched over the bristles it tends to split and break. Use a vent brush or a brush with widely spaced prongs instead of a bristle brush.
- Never brush wet hair as it is more likely to split.
- Always use a comb to untangle knots.
- To keep brushes clean, dissolve a tablespoon of soda in a basin of hot water. Add a little antiseptic and leave for five minutes. Rinse under warm running water.

25

HALF TAIL

1 When your hair is loose, section off the top layer by sliding your thumbs under the hair above your ears. Gather the hair together at the back of your head in a ponytail. Fasten the ponytail with a covered elastic band.

tip *Comb out any tangles first so that your fingers slide easily through your hair.*

2 Brush the tail and back lengths until they're smooth. Use hairspray to control any stray wisps, smoothing them into place with the palms of your hands.

tip *If your hair looks dull, add extra shine by stroking wax over your hair.*

3 Choose a simple ribbon to match your outfit, wind it round the base of the ponytail and tie it in a bow. Alternatively, make a separate bow and attach it to your ponytail with several hair grips.

tip *Don't try to secure your ponytail with ribbon alone as it will slide out, especially if your hair is freshly washed.*

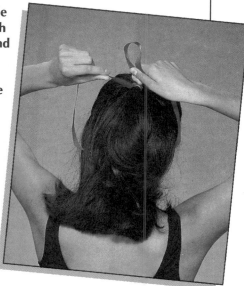

HAIR STYLING PROJECT 5: 5 WAYS WITH PONYTAILS

• TECHNIQUE 6 •

GOING BLONDE

Going blonde is a big decision. But if you fancy taking the plunge, HAIR STYLING will give you the vital confidence and know-how to do it successfully yourself.

If you want to go blonde, the choice is between highlighting your hair and having a full-head tint. Highlighting is more subtle and can produce either a sun-kissed look or more dramatic streaks. Tinting has a bolder effect and leads to a competely new look.

HIGHLIGHTS

TECHNIQUE **6** of HAIR STYLING gives you a step-by-step guide to highlighting your hair at home.

The strand test

It is essential to do a strand test on a piece of hair before attempting highlights. This will help you determine how long the process will take, as this can vary considerably. Your hair may lighten at a faster rate if it is permed or straightened.

Colour a fine strand from the under-layers of your hair, following the directions on the packet. Always wear plastic gloves when using dye and keep the mixture away from your face and eyes. Keep the developing strand away from the rest of the hair by clipping it over a tissue.

After 15 minutes, wipe off the mixture with cotton wool and assess the colour. (Brown hair turns red and then orange before it goes blonde.) In most cases, you'll need to re-apply the mixture and continue checking every 15 minutes until the hair is the colour you want. Note how long the process takes.

BEFORE

1 Brush your hair into its normal style. Prepare the highlighting mixture according to the instructions on the packet.

tip *Cover your clothes with an old towel. You can protect the towel with cling film.*

PREPARATION

TIME *45-120 minutes*

HAVE TO HAND
• hair brush • highlighting kit
• two towels • plastic gloves
• fine-toothed comb • hair dryer with diffuser • mixing bowl • watch • shampoo • conditioner

27

2 Kits usually supply a cap with holes in it through which you pull the strands of hair you wish to colour. You can also apply the mixture freehand with a fine-toothed comb. Use it like a pen to draw the dye down a few strands of hair with the top two teeth. This is the best way of highlighting hair that is quite long.

HIGHLIGHTING TIME GUIDE

Natural hair colour	Development time
Blonde	15-30 minutes
Mousey	20-40 minutes
Mid-brown	40-90 minutes

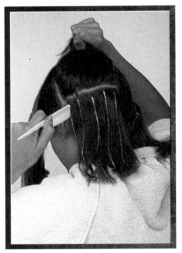

3 Always begin with areas of dark hair first. Start with the underneath and work up through the hair in 2.5-5cm (1-2in) 'layers'.

tip To achieve the best results, get a friend to help you do the back. Even if you use a highlighting cap, it's still difficult to see all the holes.

4 Pay special attention to the area around your parting. The dye should begin as close as possible to the roots. Use the tail of the comb for extra precision.

tip The further apart you place the highlights, the more subtle they will appear.

5 Use a diffuser dryer on the coolest, slowest setting for extra warmth. Keep it moving and start timing. Check the colour 15 minutes before the process should be complete.

tip Warmth speeds up colouring. If you don't have a diffuser, wear a plastic shower cap.

WATCHPOINTS

• After the lightening process wavy hair may seem slightly straighter than before.
• Most hair passes through red and orange before it eventually turns a paler shade, so don't panic if your test strand looks an alarming colour.
• Check that your skin is not allergic or hypersensitive to the chemicals by applying a tiny amount of mixture to a small patch of clean skin just behind the ear or in the crease of your elbow 48 hours before you intend to colour your hair. Check there is no reaction.
• It is best to avoid highlighting if your hair is particularly dark, as the extended processing time required may damage its condition. Dark hair will look much subtler if it is low-lighted instead. The technique remains the same, but the 'lights' are warm reddish instead of blonde.
• Throw away any unused highlighting mixture. It loses its potency after two hours and, if the mixture is covered and stored, its chemical deterioration could cause the container to explode.

6 When you've got to the desired shade, rinse off the mixture and shampoo your hair. Apply conditioner, work it into the hair and leave it for at least two minutes before rinsing.

tip If you are using a highlighting cap, keep it on until you have rinsed off all traces of colourant, then remove the cap and shampoo the whole head.

HAIR STYLING TECHNIQUE 6: HIGHLIGHTS

• PROJECT 6 •

FULL-HEAD TINT

BEFORE

If you're convinced that you want a complete change of hair colour, or you simply want to enhance the richer colours that are in your hair already, PROJECT 6 of HAIR STYLING shows you how to treat yourself to a full-head tint.

PREPARATION

TIME 15-90 minutes

HAVE TO HAND
• tint kit • butterfly clips • fine-toothed comb • mixing bowl • plastic gloves • cotton wool • polythene hood • two towels • shampoo • conditioner • hairdryer

1 Do the strand test before you start. Section your hair into quarters. Part the hair in the middle, then horizontally across the crown from just behind the ears. Protect your clothes with a towel.

tip *Don't use metal grips to hold the hair – aluminium and stainless steel are exceptions.*

2 Wearing plastic gloves, apply the mixture, starting about 2.5cm (1in) away from the roots. Work up from the bottom layers in 2cm (³/₄ in) horizontal partings.

tip *The darkest hair is usually at the back of the head, so treat this area first and apply the mixture with your fingers.*

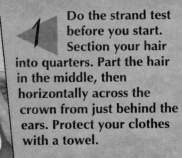

29

3 Leave to process for about half the time indicated by your strand test.

 tip *To check that the lightening process has reached the same point as the test, take a strand of hair and wipe it clean with a piece of cotton wool.*

4 Begin applying the mixture to the root area, again in horizontal 2cm ($^3/_4$in) partings. Apply directly to the hair, then spread and work in well with your fingers.

tip *As usual, treat the darkest area of hair first.*

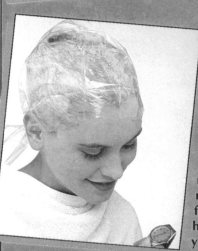

5 Place a polythene hood over your hair and time the second half of the lightening process. After the correct time, check the colour of one strand. If it is not light enough, replace the mixture and repeat the check every five minutes until your hair is the colour you want.

6 Remove the polythene hood. Rinse your hair well with tepid water and then shampoo thoroughly with a mild shampoo.

tip *Ensure that all traces of colourant have been completely removed from the hair.*

7 Apply conditioner, then blow dry your hair into the style you want.

tip *Processed hair needs gentle treatment, so choose rich conditioners. Never use your dryer on its hottest setting and keep it moving all the time.*

PROBLEM •SOLVER•

RE-DYEING

• If you don't like your highlights, don't panic. They always look their brightest when they are first done and will tone down after about a week. If you're still unhappy, you can always camouflage them using a permanent dye in a shade that matches your natural hair colour. It is best, however, to ask a professional for advice first.

• As your hair colour grows out and your real colour shows at the roots, follow steps 4-6 of the Project again. If you're bored with being blonde, use highlights to help you grow out a blonde full-head tint.

• Coloured hair may lose some of its elasticity and strength due to the hydrogen peroxide attacking the hair protein. If this happens, the hair is not permanently 'ruined'. The effects are limited to the treated area so that future regrowth is unaffected. You should not, however, re-dye your hair if the condition is severe.

WATCHPOINTS

• Don't apply dye if your scalp is irritated or has any cuts, scratches or sores. Never use the dye mixture on eyelashes or brows.

• Wait at least one day after washing your hair before colouring it, otherwise the scalp may feel itchy or irritated.

HAIR STYLING PROJECT 6: FULL-HEAD TINT

• TECHNIQUE 7 •

USING TONGS

Tonging is a quick and effective heat-styling technique, allowing you to experiment with a variety of looks for day and evening. In Technique 7, we show you how to use tongs for best results.

BEFORE

PREPARATION

TIME *approx 15 minutes (depending on hair length)*

HAVE TO HAND
• butterfly clips • heat styling lotion • tongs • hair grips • comb • fabric hair twist • hair pins

---

2 ▼▼▼▼▼▼
After you have tonged a section of hair, wind the curl around your forefinger and pin it in place with a hair grip. When you have fastened all the curls with grips, leave them to cool, and mist with styling spray before releasing them.

1 ▲▲▲▲▲▲
Use slim-barrelled tongs to achieve maximum curl. Clip back the sides and lower layers of hair and start by tonging the hair at the crown. Wind the hair length along the barrel of the tongs to form ringlets.

tip For spiral ringlets, slide the tongs into the hair about 2.5cm (1in) from the roots. Wind the hair in an S–shaped spiral.

tip Check that all the curls are cool to touch before you finger-comb, or they will simply drop out!

3 ▶▶▶▶▶▶
When you release each curl, gently back-comb small sections of hair at the roots to add volume. Tease out the ringlets at the crown to soften them and arrange them on your forehead. Complete the look by drawing up your hair at the sides and fastening it with hair clips or decorative combs. Allow the curls at the crown to tumble forwards across your forehead.

tip Don't comb through your ringlets or they may lose their definition.

31

• PROJECT 7 •

3 WAYS WITH TONGS

Discover the versatility of tongs. Use them to create a mass of curls, ringlets or soft waves on clean, dry hair, or simply to revive tired hair between washes.

1 SWEPT-BACK CHIC

1 Start by combing your hair, which should be both clean and dry. Leaving the bottom layer loose, gather up the top layers and fasten them out of the way with butterfly clips or hair grips. Further divide the bottom layer into 2.5cm (1in) sections.

★ **tip** *Sectioning keeps your hair under control, so that you can style each hair strand.*

2 Spray the hair strands with heat styling lotion and comb the lotion through your hair. Wind each section of hair over the tongs, holding for a few seconds until your hair flicks up at the ends.

★ **tip** *Always use a heat styling lotion to protect hair from heat damage caused by tonging.*

3 Release a section of hair from a butterfly clip and divide the hair further into 1cm ($\frac{1}{2}$in) sections. Spray the hair strands with heat styling lotion and then wind the hair around the tong barrel. Repeat this technique for the rest of your hair. Lastly, sweep your hair up in a wave with hair grips or decorative combs.

32

2 MANE OF CURLS

1 Use butterfly clips to pin up all but the lower sections of hair. Divide the lower sections of hair further into 2.5cm (1in) hair widths and wind them over the barrel of the tongs. Hold for a few seconds and release.

2 Continue tonging the rest of your hair, working your way up to the crown. Curl your fringe last, tonging random sections to add volume.

★ **tip** *Don't wind the barrel of the tongs closer than 1cm (½in) to your hair roots, or you may burn your scalp.*

TRICKS — of the trade

● **Use the barrel of your tongs as a guide to the amount of hair you should curl at any one time. If your hair section** is wider than the barrel, the heat won't penetrate the hair properly.

● **When tonging, make sure that the hair ends are held between the barrel and the lever. If the hair ends stick out, they may end up looking oddly crimped or frizzy.**

3 When you have tonged your whole head of hair, leave it to cool before misting with hair spray to hold the curls in place.

★ **tip** *If your hair doesn't curl the first time, rewind a smaller amount along the barrel of the tongs. Don't hold the curl for more than 60 seconds.*

4 Gently run your fingers through your hair from the roots to the ends to break up the ringlets and give a softer look.

★ **tip** *If you want looser curls, wrap thicker sections of hair over and along the tong barrel.*

33

1 Using both hands, gather your hair into a pony-tail at the nape of your neck. Fasten the pony-tail with a fabric hair twist.

⭐ *tip* *Use hair grips to pin back any short wisps of hair.*

3 CURLY PONY-TAIL

PROBLEM
• SOLVER •

GETTING HAIR TO CURL

• If your hair won't curl, check that the brush has had enough time to heat up properly and, if you are using steam tongs, that there is enough water in the barrel of the tongs.

• To master the art of tonging, practise wrapping sections of hair smoothly around the tong barrel with the tongs switched off. To discover how long it takes for your hair to curl, heat up the tongs and time-test a single strand, working up from two to twenty seconds.

• If your hair is very long, the sheer weight may drag it down, making the curls drop out. To help them set, secure the curls in place with hair grips until they have cooled.

• Never attempt to use hot tongs on wet or damp hair. Tonging works best on clean, dry hair.

• Use steam tongs if your hair is damaged by perming or bleaching, as these are kinder on dry hair.

2 Start curling your pony-tail by bringing 1cm (½in) sections of hair around to one side, and wind them over the tong barrel. Be patient – the smaller the section of hair, the tighter the curls.

⭐ *tip* *Shake your head from side to side to loosen the curls.*

3 If you have a fringe, use the tongs to curl random sections of hair. Wind the hair round the tongs so that it curls back off your face. Finger-comb the curls lightly and mist with hairspray.

⭐ *tip* *Avoid sectioning your fringe before tonging as this leaves visible gaps.*

• TECHNIQUE 8 •

PERMING

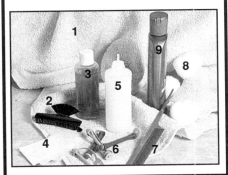

BEFORE

A perm gives you a head of fabulous curls, which look great without the need to spend hours styling. Technique 8 gives you the confidence to perm your hair at home, like a professional. Simply follow the step-by-step instructions to successful perming for medium-length hair.

PREPARATION

TIME *45 minutes*

HAVE TO HAND
1 towels **2** plastic grips or butterfly clips perming kit (including **3** perming lotion, **4** end papers and **5** neutraliser) **6** perming rods **7** plastic tail comb **8** cotton wool **9** shampoo

1 ▶▶▶▶▶▶▶▶▶▶
    Shampoo your hair and blot it dry with a towel. Don't use conditioner when you wash your hair as this coats the hair strands, inhibiting the absorption of perming lotion.

★ *tip* *Before you begin, place an old towel over your shoulders to protect your clothes from the perming chemicals, which can have a bleaching effect.*

35

2

Comb your hair with a plastic tail comb and divide it into sections that are slightly narrower than the width of your perming rods. Fasten each section out of the way with plastic grips or butterfly clips.

tip *If your hands are sensitive, wear plastic gloves to protect them from the perming chemicals.*

3

Unpin the front section of hair and use the tail comb to part your hair 1cm (¹/₂in) back from your hairline. Dip a pad of cotton wool in perming solution and stroke it along the hair lengths. Pin up the section of hair again and repeat on the next section.

tip *Use about half of the solution to pre-soak all your hair.*

4

Starting at the front, release a section of hair and comb it smooth. Hold the hair taut and fold the end paper over the hair strands close to the roots. Slide the end paper along the hair strands to the ends, without letting any hair slip out.

tip *It's best to have a trim before perming as uneven hair ends won't curl easily.*

WATCHPOINTS

TEST CURLS

• Perming can have unpredictable results, so even experienced professionals perform test curls before treating the whole head of hair. At home, a test curl helps you assess whether your hair is in suitable condition for perming, and which perming rods will give you the best curl.

• All home perming kits include instructions on how to perform a test curl. (Remember, the development time for the test curl may be different from the development time for the complete perm.)

• If the hair shows any sign of damage, such as softening or stickiness, its condition is too poor to risk perming. Rinse the hair well, neutralise, rinse again, and forget about perming until the general condition of

your hair improves. If the hair is not damaged, continue perming according to the manufacturer's instructions, but avoid re-perming the test area.

• Before perming, carefully read the instructions on the perming kit leaflet. Different perming kit brands contain different chemical compounds, so instructions and timing can vary considerably.

• Perming chemicals should be kept away from metal. Use a plastic comb and plastic butterfly clips and remove metal jewellery and glasses.

• If you are considering both perming and colouring your hair, have the perm first since the chemicals can bleach artificial hair colours. Wait at least a week between processes. Do not perm partially coloured or highlighted hair since the chemicals will affect the different textures in different ways.

• Foam perming solutions do not require pre-soaking before washing.

TRICKS —
— *of the trade*

• *Make sure that you have enough lotion for your hair. Thick shoulder-length hair may require two home perming kits.*

• *Home perming kits don't include perming rods. You need about 40-50 rods for normal hair and up to 80 for very thick or long hair. The size and the shape of the rods determine the size and shape of the curl.*

• *For professional results, choose straight cylindrical rods (similar to mini-rollers). Rods with 1cm (¹/₂ in) diameter are the most popular. Run a test curl to see how your hair reacts.*

• *End papers help smooth out stray ends. If a hair section has two separate lengths, it is best to treat them separately.*

HAIR STYLING TECHNIQUE 8: PERMING

Foam perms

Foam perms are easier to use at home than conventional perming lotions. The advantage of a foam perm is that the hair strands don't require pre-soaking. Like perming lotions, however, the perming solution tends to drip as the foam disappears, so always wear an old towel over your shoulders to protect your clothes as the chemicals can bleach fabric.

To use perming foam, wind sections of clean, towel-dried hair on to the perming rods. Spray perming foam along the length of each rod. Once the development time has elapsed, rinse the hair in water while it's still in the rods. Pat dry and apply foam neutraliser. Remove the rods and massage the remaining neutraliser into your hair. Rinse your hair.

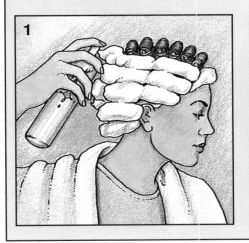

5
Holding the hair taut, place the first perming rod under the end paper. Roll the hair smoothly and evenly around the perming rod until the rod sits against the scalp. Secure it by placing the attached elasticated strap over the perming rod.

tip *Don't let the strap sit under the perming rod, where the hair is not supported, as it can leave an indent on the hair strands.*

6
Continue binding your hair strands with end papers and winding these sections around the rods. Place a strip of cotton wool across your forehead to soak up any drips of perming lotion. Apply the remaining half of perming lotion over the perming rods.

tip *If you have sensitive skin, smear Vaseline or cold cream around your hairline before positioning the cotton wool.*

PROBLEM ·SOLVER·

Most home-perming problems are due to not following instructions properly.

FRIZZY HAIR
If your hair looks curly when wet but dries to a frizz, it has lost its elasticity. The most common reason is over-processing. Keep the hair well-conditioned and avoid further processing until the hair has grown sufficiently for the damaged hair to be trimmed.

OVER-CURLY HAIR
If the result is curlier than you expected, you probably used curling rods or hair sections that were too small. Counteract the curl with heavy-duty conditioners and brush your hair smooth when blow-drying.

BRITTLE, BROKEN HAIR
Either your hair wasn't in good enough condition to perm in the first place, or the perming solution was left on for too long. Once the damage has reached this level, the only solution is to have your hair cut very short and to keep it short until the damaged hair has grown out. Keep using intensive conditioning treatments to improve hair condition.

LACK OF CURL
This may be due to using the wrong perming kit for your hair type or, more likely, to the way you used the perming rods. You may have rolled too much hair around them. Don't re-perm your hair. Go to a salon for advice, or use curl-boosting sprays, setting lotions and bendy rollers until re-perming is possible.

Did you know...?
• The first modern permanent wave method was devised in 1905. This depended on the use of curling rods attached to a machine.

37

HAIR STYLING TECHNIQUE 8: PERMING

7
▲▲▲▲▲▲▲▲

Leave the perming solution to develop for the recommended time. When the developing time has elapsed, remove the cotton-wool strips. Using a shower attachment, rinse the perming rods with warm water for at least two minutes.

⭐ *tip* *Use a powerful jet of water to rinse the perming solution out of your hair.*

8
▲▲▲▲▲▲▲▲

Gently pat your hair dry with a towel and squeeze the perming rods to remove excess water.

⭐ *tip* *Make sure you remove as much water as possible. If your hair is wet when you apply neutraliser, the solution will become too diluted to be effective.*

9
▲▲▲▲▲▲▲▲

Place fresh cotton wool around the hairline. Apply neutraliser by guiding the nozzle along the length of each perming rod. Cover your whole head of hair. Leave the neutraliser to develop for the recommended time.

⭐ *tip* *Neutaliser sets the hair strands into the desired shape by hardening and shrinking the hair shaft.*

After perming

- Don't shampoo too soon after perming or the curl may be lost. Wait at least a day.
- Use extra rich conditioners after washing. Look for conditioners marked 'dry/permed' or 'colour treated'.
- Throw away all unused lotions as they won't keep.
- If your hair feels particularly dry, try an intensive conditioning treatment once a fortnight.
- Use heated styling aids with care. If possible, allow your hair to dry naturally.
- Your hair may take a few days to settle down after perming.
- Don't re-perm hair if you're not happy with the results.
- Use a diffuser attachment on your hairdryer as this helps to promote the curls. Diffusers disperse the air and therefore are kinder to your hair.
- Use a water spray every morning to revitalise the curls.

10
▲▲▲▲▲▲▲

Release each strap and unwind the perming rods without pulling or stretching the curls. Massage the remaining neutraliser into your hair with your fingertips.

⭐ *tip* *Avoid tugging at your curls as this may cause them to fall out.*

11
▲▲▲▲▲▲▲

Rinse your hair with fresh water. DO NOT use shampoo. Apply a rich conditioner, then scrunch-dry with a diffuser or leave your hair to dry naturally.

⭐ *tip* *Once it is dry, use an Afro comb or your fingers to add lift and definition to specific curls.*

HAIR STYLING TECHNIQUE 8: PERMING

• TECHNIQUE 9 •
ATTACHING A HAIR PIECE

If you've always fancied having long hair but have never had the patience to grow it, follow the step-by-step instructions in Technique 9 and learn how to attach a false hair piece. Thanks to the introduction of synthetic fibres, they're less expensive and more realistic than ever.

1 ▲▲▲▲▲▲▲▲▲

Wash, towel dry and comb your hair. Gather your damp hair up into a tail at the crown and secure it with a covered elastic band. Divide the tail in two and pull both sections apart to tighten the hair band and ensure that your hair lies flat against your scalp.

BEFORE

PREPARATION

TIME 15 minutes
HAVE TO HAND
• comb • two covered elastic hair bands • hair piece • hair pins or grips

2 ▲▲▲▲▲▲▲

Hold the hair piece in front of your ponytail and, using a second hair band, bind the hair piece to the base of your ponytail.

⭐ *tip* *Don't wind the band securing your ponytail around the hair piece, or you'll lose the tension at the hairline.*

3 ◄◄◄◄◄◄◄◄

Separate a 2.5cm (1in) strand of hair from the hair piece and wind it around the base of your ponytail to hide both covered elastic bands. Secure the end of the hair strand with a hair pin or grip.

⭐ *tip* *If the point where the hair piece is attached to the crown is still visible, wind a second hair strand round the base.*

39

• PROJECT 8 •

4 WAYS WITH HAIR PIECES

Once you've got the hang of attaching a hair piece, try out these four fabulous styles. There are endless variations on the theme and you'll be surprised at just how easy it is to adapt your look to suit your mood and the occasion.

HIGH BUN

1 Gather up your hair into a smooth ponytail and attach the hair piece as before. Wrap the entire length of the hair piece round the elasticated hair band at the crown to make a bun. Keep the tension even but don't wind it too tightly or you may dislodge the hair piece from the point where it is attached.

tip *For a smooth finish, first comb the hair piece.*

2 Tuck the ends of the hair piece under the bun and fasten them with hair pins. To hold the style in place, insert hair pins round the bun at approximately 2.5cm (1in) intervals.

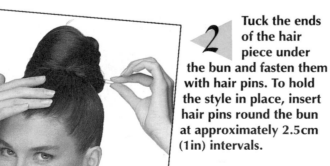

tip *For a softer look, start with a looser ponytail and back-comb your hair at the crown.*

3 Take a long scarf and wrap it round the base of the bun. Cross over the ends of the scarf at the front before tying them in a single knot at the back. Tuck the loose ends under the bun.

tip *If you do manage to achieve a neat finish, use decorative clips and slides instead.*

40

LONG PLAIT

1 Wash, towel dry and comb your hair. Tie back your hair while it is still damp in a tight ponytail at the nape of the neck. Attach a loose hair piece at the nape of the neck just above your ponytail.

⭐ ***tip*** *While your hair is still damp, smooth down any stray strands with wax or gel.*

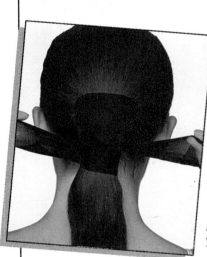

2 Hide the point where the real and false hair meet by binding a length of stocking round the join before fastening it in a double knot.

⭐ ***tip*** *Nylon stockings and tights hold the hair well as they grip the strands. When you ladder a pair of tights, save them for your hair.*

3 Plait the hair piece from the base to about 5-8cm (2-3in) from the hair ends. Secure the plait with an elasticated fabric hair twist. Lastly, cover the stocking at the nape of your neck by wrapping a decorative ribbon or scarf along its length.

⭐ ***tip*** *Keep the plaiting tension loose but even, otherwise the plait will look messy.*

TRICKS — —of the trade
HAIR PIECE CARE

● When cleaning your synthetic hair piece, brush it first to remove any hairspray residue and tangles.

● Immerse the hair piece in soapy water and soak for five to ten minutes before rinsing.

● Hair conditioners won't benefit your hair piece, but fabric conditioner will. Add to the final rinse.

● After washing, don't wring out the hair piece. Blot it dry with a towel and place it on a flat surface or a stand to help it keep its shape. Allow the synthetic hair to drip-dry. Don't comb your hair piece when it's wet. Leave it to dry naturally before brushing it.

● Don't attempt to re-style synthetic hair. If you want a curlier hair piece, buy one.

HAIR STYLING

LOOSE FALL

1 Wash, towel dry and comb your hair. Brush your hair back off your face and smooth it down with the palms of your hands.

tip *If you have short layers, pin them back with hair grips or hair pins, or smooth them into place with wax or gel.*

2 Tilt your head forwards and pull a wide fabric headband over your head to sweep the hair off your forehead. Brush the lengths of your hair again.

tip *If you have a fringe, either tuck it neatly under the headband or leave it free.*

WATCHPOINTS

• When buying a hair piece, it's important to get a good colour match. Always check the colour of the hair piece against your own hair, in both natural and artificial light.

• Don't try to adjust the colour of your hair piece yourself. This is a job best left to the professionals. Ask your salon for advice.

• Wearing a hair piece or wig is like wearing a hat, as the scalp sweats underneath. When you remove a hair piece or wig, always wash your hair.

• Clean your synthetic hair piece at least once a fortnight. Synthetic hair can be washed in ordinary shampoo and cold water. Follow the manufacturer's instructions. Real hair wigs, however, need special cleaning fluids.

• If you frequently wear a hair piece, take care not to pull your hair too tightly when scraping it back off your face in a tight ponytail. Long-term and repeated pulling can cause your hair to fall out.

3 Slide the combs attached to the hair piece into your hair behind the headband. Don't rely on them to hold the hair piece securely. Fasten the hair piece in position with hair pins. Insert a hair pin every 2.5cm (1in) around the band.

tip *To secure a hair pin, slide it forwards and then double it back on itself.*

42

HAIR STYLING PROJECT 8: 4 WAYS WITH HAIR PIECES

TUMBLING CURLS

1 Comb the hair flat and part your hair from ear to ear. Gather up the back section of hair and twist and pin it flat against the back of your head.

tip *Expect to use about six to eight pins to hold your hair in place, more if your hair is particularly fine or heavy.*

2 If your hair is straight, roughly tong the front section so that it blends with the curly hair piece.

tip *Don't attempt to tong the synthetic hair piece. It cannot withstand intense heat. If you want a curly hair piece, it is best to buy one.*

3 Hold the curly hair piece in position at the crown and pin it in place. Cover the join with strands of your own hair.

tip *If your hair is not long enough to hide the point where the real and false hair meet, use hair accessories such as hair bands, decorative grips and hair slides.*

4 Style your hair by pinning random strands of hair away from your face to create a natural, tousled look. Use a hair pin to tease out individual curls.

tip *Don't brush your hair or it will lose its curl and appear frizzy.*

43

HAIR STYLING PROJECT 8: 4 WAYS WITH HAIR PIECES

Hair extensions

BEFORE

Synthetic hair extensions are woven into the hair at the roots. This is a tricky technique, and not something you should attempt to do yourself at home. It takes two professionals about two to three hours to weave in a full head of extensions, which will last for about three months, depending on how quickly your hair grows. It is possible, however, to have less than a full head of extensions. Half heads, nape sections for ponytails and single pieces are also available and are less

expensive. In addition, some salons offer different textures of hair extensions, from tightly curled dreadlocks to coils and loops.

To attach a hair extension, the hairdresser divides the hair into small sections and weaves it into a four-stem braid. The extension is then heat-sealed to your hair.

The extensions can be left long or cut to length. Hair extensions can also be coloured to blend perfectly with your natural

hair colour. Unlike false hair pieces, you can curl or straighten extensions as you wish. Teflon-coated tongs, heated rollers, hot brushes and blowdryers are all suitable, but avoid direct contact with hot metal.

Hair extensions can be removed in the salon or taken out at home. Simply twist the plastic heat seal between your fingers until it cracks. As it breaks, peel the seal away and unravel the four-stem braids to separate the extensions from your own hair.

Suit yourself

An at-a-glance guide to finding the right hair piece for your hair type and how to wear it.

SYNTHETIC HAIR PIECES
Advantages:
- Machine-made and therefore inexpensive.
- Light and comfortable to wear.
- Easy to clean.

Disadvantages:
- Difficult to re-style.
- Difficult to alter the colour to match your natural hair.

ASIAN HAIR WIGS
Advantages:
- Machine-made and therefore inexpensive.
- Easy to re-style.

EUROPEAN HAIR WIGS
Advantages:
- Easy to style.
- Comfortable and light to wear.
- Easy to clean.

Disadvantages:
- Hand-made and therefore expensive.

LAYERED CURLY HAIR
To attach a false ponytail, it's important to smooth your own hair at the sides to give a sleek finish. Tie the back lengths into a ponytail at the nape of the neck and use wax or gel to smooth down the top and sides.

BLUNT-CUT BOB
Tie back your hair into two neat ponytails, one just below the crown, the other positioned below it, just above the nape. Secure the hair piece on top. If your hair is straight, choose a hair piece that is shaggy rather than curly, otherwise the contrast between curled back lengths and a smooth crown will look unnatural.

AFRO HAIR
Ringlets, tightly curled cascades, ponytails and wet-look hair pieces are all available. They're secured in the usual way, so your own hair shouldn't be too short.

HAIR STYLING PROJECT 8: 4 WAYS WITH HAIR PIECES

• TECHNIQUE 10 •

PUTTING YOUR HAIR UP

If you dress up to go out for the evening, why neglect your hair? In Technique 10 we have simplified a classic pleat – all you have to do is follow these seven steps to success.

BEFORE

PREPARATION

TIME *15 minutes*

HAVE TO HAND
- gel • hair brush • hair clips

1 ▲▲▲▲▲▲▲▲

Apply a little gel to straighten the hair and to hold it lightly. Make sure that it is evenly distributed by working the gel in with your fingers and then brushing your hair.

★ *tip* *Use a small amount of gel to smooth down any hairs that stick up and those at the nape of the neck. These are the parts that will really show up when the style is completed.*

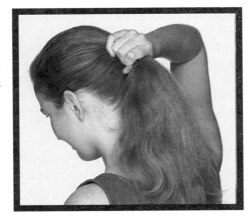

2 ◀◀◀◀◀◀◀◀◀

Brush your hair into a ponytail, but don't secure it with a band, simply hold it with your hand. Make sure the ponytail is fairly central on the back of your head.

★ *tip* *Brush your hair and pull the ponytail back tightly, as it will inevitably loosen during styling. If it is allowed to slacken the pleat will be less secure.*

45

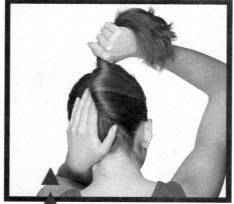

3 ▲▲▲▲▲▲▲

Hold the ponytail loosely in your left hand, then brush it sideways over the hand making sure that no strands break free.

⭐ *tip* *Don't skimp on the preliminary brushing as this look requires an ultra-smooth finish.*

4 ▲▲▲▲▲▲▲

Use your right hand to turn your hair upwards, twisting the ponytail up towards the crown. Hold your left hand along the crease to keep the style smooth and in place.

⭐ *tip* *Make sure you get the tension right. A twist that is too tight will make it difficult to tuck the ends in, but a very loose twist will be hard to secure.*

5 ▲▲▲▲▲▲▲

Carry on twisting to the end of your ponytail, moving your left hand upwards as you go to stop the pleat falling down.

⭐ *tip* *If you find your hair is coming loose as you twist, take it in stages. As you twist with your right hand, pinch in that section with your left as you move your right hand up ready to twist again.*

PROBLEM
•SOLVER•

PERFECTING YOUR TECHNIQUE

- *It takes practice to get an immaculate finish so don't be discouraged if you don't get it right the first time. For your first few attempts, don't even try to create a perfect finish. Instead, miss out the gelling step and just use your brush and hands to practise twisting in the right direction – this way you'll feel the correct tension for your hair, find out how to tuck the ends back into the pleat without disturbing the style, and learn how to insert the clips correctly.*

- *Once you've mastered the basic technique, the finishing stages will be much easier. It's important to achieve a clean line between the pleat and the opposite side of the hair – remember you can always lift the pleat a little to tuck any stray hairs under. If you find a neat line hard to produce at first, just conceal the join with a row of diamante slides, which will hide any mistakes while adding an extra, glamorous touch.*

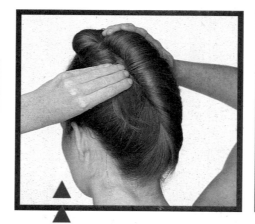

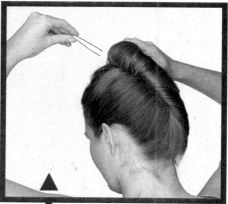

6 ▲▲▲▲▲▲▲

When you have reached the end, curve the twisted ponytail back on itself and slightly lift your pleat to gently tuck the end under. Make sure you keep your right hand firmly on the front of the twist.

⭐ *tip* *The roll at the top will be fairly secure at this point, as it should be supporting itself, but keep holding it in place with your right hand until it is secured with pins.*

7 ▲▲▲▲▲▲▲

Use clips to secure your hair down the length of your pleat. Insert them diagonally into the main body of the pleat, then angle them down to the fold and push them in as far as they'll go. This holds them more firmly than simply pushing them in from one side.

⭐ *tip* *The number of clips you use depends on the tightness of the pleat and the length of your hair.*

HAIR STYLING TECHNIQUE 10: PUTTING YOUR HAIR UP

• PROJECT 9 •

4 WAYS TO DRESS YOUR HAIR
ROLLED-UNDER CHIGNON

1 Apply gel and brush your hair smooth. Draw it back into a ponytail just above the nape and secure with a covered hair band.

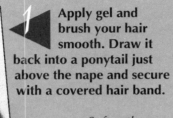

tip *Soften the front view by leaving one section of the ponytail free, brush it smooth and allow it to drape gently around the forehead.*

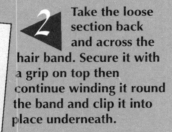

2 Take the loose section back and across the hair band. Secure it with a grip on top then continue winding it round the band and clip it into place underneath.

tip *Don't worry if your hair looks a bit messy under the band – it won't show when you've finished.*

3 Brush the ponytail through to keep it smooth, and add just a touch more gel to make your hair easier to work with.

tip *For added neatness, tuck the ends of the tail under and hold in place with a second hair band.*

4 Holding the ends of the ponytail with both hands, roll it under once and secure it with grips. Slide them through the loop you've created with the second hair band. Then tease out the new fold to conceal the under section. Finish the style by using a decorative slide or a comb just above the chignon.

47

ROLLED TOPKNOT

► Apply gel and gather your hair into a ponytail high at the crown. Start to twist the tail loosely to the end. When the tail is fully twisted, hold the end and draw it around to the back. Tuck the end under and secure it with hair clips.

tip *Turn your head upside-down and brush downwards as you make the ponytail. This ensures an extra smooth finish at the back and the* sides. Keep the twisting and coiling process fairly loose, so as to make the knot as full and soft as possible.

WATCHPOINTS

• When you have completed putting your hair up, make sure you deal with any flyaway hairs.

Add a light mist of spray when the pleat is secured. Draw a comb lightly across the surface of your hair as you direct the stray ends towards the back of your head.

Suit yourself

You can achieve a variation on the classic pleat whatever your hair style.

FRINGES

If your fringe is at an annoying length and isn't quite long enough to incorporate into the pleat you have several options. You can gel it, comb it sleekly to one side and set it with some wet-look gel. Alternatively, you can blow dry it backwards around a small circular brush for a smart quiff. Or you can even try twisting small sections of hair around your finger to create neat kiss-curls. Or scrunch it into curls for a full, softening effect.

WAVY HAIR

Damp your hair down, apply gel and blow dry straight before you start. As well as straightening your hair out, those smoothed-down waves will give the hair extra body so making it easier to work with and eliminating any need for back combing.

LONG LAYERS

A pleated roll won't be difficult to produce as long as your layers at the sides and nape are long enough to meet at the back of your head, with a few inches to spare, to allow you to pin it up.

SHORTER LAYERS

If you find layered hair coming loose at the nape, sides and fringe, don't despair, you can still have a softer version of the pleat. Simply gel the strands that have fallen loose and twist them round your finger into soft tendrils.

ASYMMETRIC SIDE TWISTS

1 Gel and brush your hair. Make a parting that curves around your head (start at one side of your forehead going diagonally to the crown then diagonally back to the side you started from at your nape). Brush the hair on one side of the parting into a ponytail and hold it with your hand two inches above and about one inch behind the point of your ear.

Twist tightly along the length, allowing the section to coil back on itself.

tip Brush the ponytail roots upwards before you start.

2 Secure your coil with plenty of grips and repeat on the other side. Smooth both down with styling spray and a fine-toothed comb.

tip Decorative combs enhance the style even further – just push them lightly into the side sections, but don't go too deep or you could disturb the hair grips that are holding the style in place.

BREAKING THE CODE

The terms used to describe different hairdressing techniques and styles can confuse the beginner. Our at-a-glance guide should put you on the right track.

BUN A roll of hair caught and secured anywhere on the head.

CHIGNON Similar to a bun but usually referring to more complicated looks involving loose rolls and twists, sometimes with loose tendrils falling from the dressed section. Also refers to a bun at the nape.

PLEAT A style is rolled and twisted round, resulting in a dividing line down the centre of the back of the head. A classic French pleat looks similar to the style in Technique 10, but uses grips to hold the hair in place at the back before it's twisted.

COTTAGE LOAF A bun at the crown or the nape, when the hair is not drawn tightly back but allowed to form a soft roll that frames the face.

BRAID A plaited section often incorporated into a dressed style.

KNOT Any bun or chignon that is literally tied like a knot or dressed to look as though it's been tied.

COIL A section of hair that is twisted and coiled, usually into a more decorative bun.

PAD Also known as a roll. A padded piece of fabric that is inserted into a section of hair to give it support or make it look fuller.

Did you know...?

• The word hairdresser originally meant just that – someone who 'dressed' hair rather than merely cutting and styling it. In the 60s and 70s the cut-and-blow dry became popular and the new generation of hair dressers were no longer taught the old dressing techniques. Today, dressed hair is becoming popular again and stylists are re-learning the old skills. Next time you visit the salon, ask your stylist for some dressing advice.

49

CHIGNON TWISTS

1 Work gel through your hair and brush it back into a ponytail secured a few inches above the neck. Separate out a thin section, 2cm (1in) wide, from the top of the tail and twist it very tightly to the end. Hold it taut away from your head as you turn. Push the section back towards your head – it will start to coil itself into an abstract squiggle. Secure the ends with grips.

2 Repeat the process with two more sections – one taken from either side of the first twist. Clip them into place and you'll have a decorated ponytail without having to use elaborate accessories. For an exquisite chignon, continue twisting sections around the outer and under sides of the tail, leaving the centre section until last as this is the area that should protrude the most from your head.

 tip For a very glamorous look, add a fine glitter ribbon or cord to each section when you are twisting the hair and incorporate it into the twist.

TRICKS
– of the trade
KEEPING YOUR HAIR SECURE

● When you want to try putting your hair up, make sure you have the right kind of clips. Professionals prefer the long, fine two-pronged styling clips, which will hold a large section of hair more securely than short clips. They are also more flexible and will not show up as much as grips.

● Often your hair is much easier to manage if it is not completely clean, so don't wash it on the day you want to try a tricky new technique. If your hair is particularly difficult to style, is very fine, or extra silky, back-combing could be the answer. Back-comb at the roots and in the underneath sections, as these won't be visible in the finished style and your hair will be pliable and less likely to flop.

WATCHPOINTS

● Don't rush the style by making the strands that you are twisting too large. Our model's hair was quite thick, so it took lots of small sections to create the look, and even the finest hair will require at least three. Finer sections are much neater if your hair isn't very long and they will be more suited to you if your hair is layered.

HAIR STYLING PROJECT 9: 4 WAYS TO DRESS YOUR HAIR

• TECHNIQUE 11 •
STYLING STRAIGHT HAIR

BEFORE

Technique 11 of HAIR STYLING shows you how to adapt a standard bob into a striking, flicked-up style which, in turn, can be transformed into an evening look in a matter of minutes.

At its best, straight hair feels silky and has a strong shine. But many of us with no hint of natural wave find styling options limited. An imaginative approach is called for! And the answer lies not only in a good cut, but also in original and exciting styling.

PREPARATION

TIME up to 30 minutes, depending on your hair's ability to hold a curl.

HAVE TO HAND
● hairdryer ● styling brush (standard or circular) ● butterfly grips ● tongs ● styling spray or hairspray ● high gloss shine spray ● leave-in conditioning spray

1 ◄◄◄◄◄◄◄◄
Dampen down your hair and section it, using butterfly clips. Dry the lower layers first by directing the nozzle of the hairdryer down the hair shaft, pulling down gently with your brush as you curl the ends under.

★ ***tip*** *Prevent your hair from heat damage by using a leave-in conditioning spray rather than water to dampen it.*

51

HAIR STYLING

2 ▲▲▲▲▲▲▲▲

Repeat on each section of hair in turn until it is smooth and sleek.

⭐ *tip* *Don't direct heat on to your fringe until the rest of your hair is dry. This very exposed area of your hair tends to be relatively dry and fine and should have as very little heat treatment as possible.*

3 ▲▲▲▲▲▲▲▲

Hair that holds curl well can be flicked up by blow drying the ends outwards round a circular brush, but dead straight hair needs much stronger measures. To curl it, apply styling spray or a light mist of water to help smooth down any flyaway hairs and to hold the ends. Then use heated tongs to curl the ends of your hair under.

4 ▲▲▲▲▲▲▲▲

To create the flicks – brush each section outwards, gripping the ends between your forefinger and middle finger. Then brush your flick-ups around your forefinger.

⭐ *tip* *For maximum curl, try to avoid curling too much hair around the brush at one time.*

PROBLEM •SOLVER•

STYLING FINE HAIR

Straight hair, whether fine and flyaway or thick and heavy, can lie very close to your head. A bit of lift at the roots can really improve a new style.

• *For soft root lift with plenty of natural movement, use heated rollers. The traditional type is probably best for you as heated bendy rollers create a curl that will relax more quickly. Never use heated rollers more than twice a week as they can be very drying.*

• *Alternatively, simply back-comb root hair to help make it stand up, and hold the shape with hairspray.*

• *As a longer-lasting solution, opt for a gentle root perm. This involves the roots being wound on very small rollers to create tight curls. When a mild lotion is used, the curl relaxes within six to eight weeks and blends in with your natural hair texture.*

• *Tong the roots using standard tongs or the*

newer type, with flat sides, that are specifically designed for this purpose. Apply styling spray sparsely to your roots and sandwich hair between the tongs.

• *Don't forget, fine straight hair may seem like a pain to style sometimes, but it is probably the easiest hair type to plait.*

TRICKS — of the trade

FLICK DRYING

If your hair is straight, drying it around a brush could be the answer to your problems, but it does take a little practice.

• **Use the dryer on a low setting so that your hair doesn't have a chance to dry before it has been styled around the brush.**

• **If you prefer a subtle flick to your hair, run an Afro comb through it after styling. This will break up the layers.**

• **If your hair is fine and fly-away, prevent static by spraying the damp ends with hairspray before flicking them up or under.**

• **For a controlled look, create tight curls, by tonging the ends of your hair when it is dry.**

• **For a cool and casual textured look, scrunch a very small blob of wax through long, flicked layers.**

52

• PROJECT 10 •

STRAIGHT HAIR VARIATIONS

Adding interest to your hair doesn't have to mean scrunching or curling. Make the most of your straight hair with decorative accessories or by changing points of interest such as the parting or fringe.

HEADBANDS

1 Headbands are ideal for taking hair off the face as well as hiding a multitude of sins – fringes that are in need of a trim, for example. Wide, stretchy headbands are also good for concealing root re-growth that tends to show up particularly quickly on tinted, straight hair.

2 Alice bands give a softer look. Just slide them back on your hair or, to add extra height at the fringe, tilt your head forwards, slide the band to just past its usual position and lift your head up while pulling the band forwards into position. This will make your fringe lift slightly.

COMBS

To take hair away from your face or simply to soften the effect, combs are perfect – they give a subtle dressed-up look for the evening as well. If your hair is very straight and silky, back-comb it a little at the sides, then pull it back and clip into place before adding the combs. This helps prevent them coming loose.

WATCHPOINTS

• Straight hair looks best when it has a healthy shine and a good cut, so make a conscious effort to get it trimmed regularly to remove split ends (which are very obvious on straight hair) and to maintain shape. Every two to 12 weeks, depending on the length and condition, should be sufficient.
• Condition your hair after every wash but avoid over-rich creams, which can be heavy and weigh the hair down. They can make it appear greasy and leave it difficult to style.
• Think ahead, make sure you choose the right styling products to promote shine. Avoid ordinary gel and strong mousse as they both have a tendency to dry your hair out and make it look dull. Instead, choose wet-look gel, shine sprays, natural-hold styling sprays and a touch of wax.

53

PONYTAIL BANDS

1 You can buy, or make, decorative ponytail bands and use lots together for an unusual effect. Here a band attached to two bobbles is twisted to form a cross, wrapped under a ponytail and threaded through the opposite side of the band. Try to co-ordinate the colour of your band to match what you're wearing.

2 Add a couple more bands to make the style look even more fun.

tip Try making your own ponytail bands or adapting one you have bought. String coloured beads together and attach them to the ponytail band.

HAIR ACCESSORIES

The simplest accessories can often be the most striking. Here a velvet scrunchie band and matching bow clip have been trimmed with gold beads and used to decorate a plait.

Make your own scrunchie band

Shop-bought scrunchie hair bands can be very expensive so why not try making one for yourself? They are so quick to make that you can easily hand sew them if you don't happen to have a sewing machine.

• Take a piece of fabric 85 x 20cm (34 x 8in) and fold it in half with the right side of the fabric on the inside.
• Sew the raw edges together, leaving a 12mm (¹/₂in) seam allowance.
• Press the seam open with an iron, making sure the seam is in the middle of the band. Carefully over-sew the edges to prevent them fraying, or cut zig-zag edges with a pair of pinking shears.
• Turn the tube you have made

inside out. If you are having problems pushing the fabric through, try attaching a safety pin to one end.
• Cut a piece of 6mm (¹/₄in) wide elastic to the size you want your scrunchie to be. Attach a safety pin to one end of the elastic, and pin the other end on to the inside seam. Push through the loose end of elastic.
• Overlap the two elastic ends and sew them tightly together using strong thread.
• Join together the two ends of fabric by tucking one end of the tube inside the other, overlapping them by at least 2.5cm (1in). Turn the raw edge under neatly.
• Finally, arrange the material evenly around the elastic and sew over the join.

Hair ties and slides

There is a vast assortment of accessories which will pep up any style and keep your hair in place at the same time. But some are kinder to hair than others.

• Never clip hair too tightly into a slide – make sure the catch can close easily.

• Slides should be flat with widely spaced prongs.
• Always use wide bands that are covered in material, such as towelling. An elastic band on its own can become entangled in the hair, damaging the hair follicle. At its most extreme, it may even cause hair to fall out.

HAIR STYLING PROJECT 10: STRAIGHT HAIR VARIATIONS

A LOW SIDE PARTING

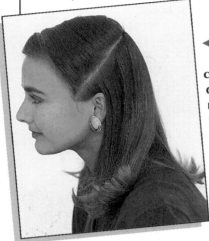

1 A low side parting adds height because the hair is combed against its natural direction of growth. It will retain its style for longer if you back-comb the roots at this stage.

 tip *Slightly greasy roots can be easily hidden by this type of parting.*

2 Twist the hair to one side, pulling tightly to make the style as neat as possible. Secure the twisted ends with a hair slide or comb.

tip *For a slightly different look, secure the ends with a row of thin gold slides.*

A CURLED-BACK FRINGE

Make a side parting to take your fringe off your face and add height. Apply styling spray, then blow dry your fringe back around a small, circular brush. When it's completely dry, brush the fringe out slightly so that it flicks softly to one side.

tip *If your hair is very fine use a vent brush to help prevent static.*

WATCHPOINTS

Many people with straight hair opt for a perm, but you should think carefully before taking this step. If your hair curls easily with ordinary stylers and is in good condition, it should be suitable for perming. If any styled-in curl drops very quickly, the same could happen when your hair is processed. Re-growth could also be a problem as the difference between permed hair and straight roots is very noticeable.

BREAKING THE CODE

These days there's a cutting technique for every hair type and style. Hair always grows unevenly and the shape of your cut will soon become ragged if left untrimmed. Regular trims will also get rid of split ends and keep the hair in good condition. Don't let your hairdresser confuse you with jargon – here are some of the more common terms.

GRADUATION
The hair is cut at an angle. The shorter lengths support upper layers and encourage a fullness, as in a wedge cut.

LAYERING
Usually hair is shorter on the top and sides and left longer at the back. Layered hair can be used for any type of hair, and, in particular, can add shape to curly hair.

BLUNT CUTTING
The hair is cut straight at the ends to fall to one length. This type of cut can make fine hair look much thicker than it really is, and is usually used on a short or shoulder length bob, with or without a fringe. Blunt cuts usually work best on straight hair, as the style is more likely to keep its shape, although wavy hair can also look good if it's dried correctly.

TAPERING
Scissors are used in a sliding action back and forth along the hair's length for a thinning effect that creates shorter layers. As well as thinning, this makes a natural curl more pronounced.

CLIPPERING
Hair is literally shaved very close to the head using special hairdressing clippers. It's usually done on short cuts to emphasise the shape of the face and neck.

55

Did you know...?

- The straightness – or waviness – of your hair is determined by the shape of your individual hair follicles. This is why some people tend to have just an isolated wavy area that contrasts with the rest of their hair.
- Straight hair lies flatter to the scalp than curly hair because of the growth pattern – it only takes a little natural wave to lift hair away from the scalp as it grows. A variety of styling aids, chemical processing and the right cut can give straight hair extra lift.
- If your straight hair is quite limp, it could be because, although fine, the hairs are quite numerous. That means there's a large number of hair follicles and a lot of oil-producing sebaceous glands to accompany them.

SOFT TENDRILS

▶ For a quick change of style that doesn't require a hairdryer, work wax or wet-look gel lightly through your hair. Wind most of the hair into a knot at the back, leaving a few tendrils loose around the hairline. Twist them and your fringe into a series of soft spikes.

The five-minute restyle

1 Spray your hair lightly with water to make it slightly easier to manage. Part it neatly across your head from ear to ear. Take the front section up on top into a ponytail (this can be at the centre or to one side). Twist the tail and coil it into a neat top knot, tucking the end under. Secure with grips.

tip For a complete change, take your fringe back, too. Back comb it at the roots. Brush it backwards and control it with hairspray. Tuck the ends of the fringe into the top knot using the end of a tail comb.

2 Vary the look slightly by giving the curls at the end of your hair more volume. Simply brush your hair, making sure that you hold it in the brush when you reach the ends. Carefully lift up the brush, taking your hair with it, and gently shake the hair free from the brush. This will give added volume to the curls.

tip To hold this slightly fluffier look in place, back-comb or back-brush the under sections of hair and lightly mist with firm-hold hairspray.

Your time is precious, and if you enjoy a few extra minutes in bed in the morning you'll appreciate the five-minute restyle, which you can try without even washing your hair.

If you often have to restyle your hair without washing it, follow these short cuts.
- A directing nozzle not only dries a section of hair very quickly, but it will also direct the heat on to the brush and prevent the rest of the style being blown out of shape.
- Don't handle your hair more than you need to, this will only help make it greasy.
- Excessive amounts of gel or mousse will also attract dirt.

• TECHNIQUE 12 •
STYLING CURLY HAIR

Curly hair is one of the strongest hair types, with lots of natural elasticity, root lift and body. It can be unruly, so in Technique 12 we show you how to style it successfully to make the most of natural curl and control frizz.

BEFORE

PREPARATION

TIME *15 minutes (depending on hair length and thickness)*

HAVE TO HAND
• leave-in conditioning spray • natural-hold mousse • infra-red lamp or hairdryer with diffuser attachment • wax styling cream or spray shine • wide-toothed comb

1 Shampoo, condition and towel dry your hair. Treat any frizzy areas, including the fringe and top layers, with a leave-in conditioning spray to help moisturise and protect the hair shafts from the effects of heat styling.

2 Use a natural-hold mousse to help hold your style. Squeeze out blobs of mousse on to your hand, then apply to your hair. Pay special attention to the lower layers, as these will support your style.

 tip *Work the mousse into your hair with your fingers. Use a wide-toothed comb to spread the mousse down the length.*

57

3

 To dry your hair without losing any curl, use an infra-red lamp. The gentle heat has the opposite effect to the smoothing function of a blow-dryer and encourages curls to form without drying out the hair.

tip *To prevent the style going flat, make sure you dry the roots thoroughly.*

4

 If you don't have an infra-red lamp, use a diffuser attachment on your hairdryer. Scrunch up your hair in the palm of your hand to help curls form. Boost the curls by pushing the diffuser up into your hair as you dry.

tip *Alternatively, use your hairdryer on its lowest heat setting.*

5

Rub a little hair wax into individual curls to give definition and help moisturise dry hair. Take care not to overload the curls round your forehead with wax or they'll look greasy.

tip *If you're not sure how much wax to use, start by trying half the amount you think you'll need.*

PROBLEM
•SOLVER•

DEALING WITH FRIZZY HAIR

• Very curly hair, especially if it has been permed, has a tendency to frizz. Minimise this with regular conditioning treatments. When you apply conditioner, wrap your hair in cling film to trap the heat from your scalp and so speed up the conditioning process. Wrap your cling film-covered head in a towel and leave for 20 to 30 minutes.

• Dry ends are a common problem for people with permed or naturally curly hair. If condi-

tioning treatment makes your hair go limp at the roots, invest in a conditioning cream or serum formulated for the ends only. Rub a few drops of serum between the palms of your hands, then massage it into the ends of your hair before you begin styling, or at intervals during the day if they feel particularly dry.

• If you brush or comb very curly hair, it tends to frizz. So try using an Afro comb, which teases the curls into shape rather than combing them out. Or, for a casual finish, just finger comb your hair.

• Moisture in the atmosphere can make your curls frizz the minute you step out of the front door. A very light mist of hairspray should prevent this happening.

HAIR STYLING TECHNIQUE 12: STYLING CURLY HAIR

• PROJECT 11 •

CURLY HAIR VARIATIONS

Although curly hair can look beautiful when it's left loose, its natural texture can also be worked into a number of different styles. And here are some surprisingly simple ideas.

PREPARATION

TIME *5 minutes*

HAVE TO HAND
● fine-toothed comb ● hair clips ● styling spray

1 Divide the front of your hair into a 7.5cm (3in) section and gently back-comb it from the ends right down to the roots.

tip *Concentrate most of the back-combing on the back of the section, with just a light touch in front. This way you won't prevent shine by ruffling the hair cuticles on the top layers.*

2 Roll the back-combed section under and secure it at the base of the roll with hair grips.

tip *Don't pull the hair roll too tight. Check the width of a large traditional roller and imagine you're winding your hair round this.*

3 Take up sections of hair of equal width from either side of your head and repeat the back-combing and rolling process. Fasten each section with hair grips, pushing them well into the roll so that they're hidden from view.

tip *To smooth down the hair strands, use styling spray and a comb.*

59

DECORATIVE TOUCHES

◄ Scarves – a twisted scarf can be used to create different effects, depending on size, colour and pattern. Take a short scarf or handkerchief under your hair at the nape of your neck and knot it on top to hold your hair off your face. Alternatively, use a longer scarf to make a large bow.

tip *Choose soft fabrics for day and stiffer, metallic ones for dramatic evening looks.*

◄ Alice bands – are a simple, easy-to-wear hair accessory. You can even try wearing two Alice bands together. Pull your hair tight off your face, or, if you want extra height at the front, pull the band back to your crown, then push it forwards into position, pushing your hair up as you go.

◄ Stretch headbands – these are fashionable and functional, helping to conceal oily roots, growing-out colour, or a frizzy fringe. You can buy elasticated headbands in a variety of colours and patterns, or make your own from a short length of strong, stretchy fabric.

Suit yourself

Here are a few suggestions to help you choose the right hairstyle for you.

SHORT CUTS

Curly hair has lots of root lift, so it often works well with a style that's trimmed short at the nape of the neck and layered on top. Blow-dry longer lengths back to make soft waves, or wax the curls on top so that they fall forwards. This is ideal for people with high foreheads, or slightly thin hair and see-through areas on the scalp.

For thicker, heavier hair, a few extra inches on top and a graduated cut from the nape of the neck to the tops of the ears shows off the hair's curly texture and helps concentrate fullness at the sides.

MID-LENGTH STYLES

Opt for one-length bobs that show off well-conditioned curls and make fine hair look thicker than it really is. Or, if your hair is very thick, you'll find greater manageability and styling flexibility if you reduce the weight with a few layers. But don't cut the layers too short on top – they might just stick up leaving you with an unbalanced style. If you like to wear a fringe, try keeping it light, and remember that the curl will make it spring up when it's dry, so don't cut it too short.

LONG HAIR

If your hair is fine, opt for a one-length style, which will help it look fuller. But remember, you'll have minimum root lift, as the weight of long hair tends to pull the hair flat. For thicker hair, a layered cut that thins rather than adds texture to your hair is probably the best option. If the layers are kept fairly long, you'll still be able to put up your hair and you may even find that the cut increases the number, and the tightness of the curls. The weight of thick hair can drag curl out in permed or natural styles, but when it is thinned out, the curl springs back up.

WISPY HAIR

If your curly hair looks wispy, try an all-over tint. The uniform colour will help make your hair look solid, and if you use a wash in wash out colourant, you can change back to your natural colour whenever you feel like it.

Did you know...?

If your curly hair lacks shine this doesn't have to mean it's in poor condition. Shine comes from light being reflected off the shafts of your hair, and when hair is straight and sleek, light is reflected more easily than when hair is curled and twisted. You can increase your hair's shine artificially by using spray-on gloss, which contains thousands of highly reflective particles. But don't use too much or your hair will look and feel greasy.

HAIR STYLING PROJECT 11: CURLY HAIR VARIATIONS

DRESSING UP HAIR

◀ Use a scrunchie hair band to hold your hair off your face in a high ponytail at the crown. Use an Afro comb or tail comb to tease your curls out at the ends. If you've got any short, stray hair strands that won't stay in a band, twist them around your finger into tendrils and leave them to frame your face.

▶ Dressing your hair high on your head is easy with curly hair. Part your hair in the middle and comb the right side over to the left. Secure it at the right of centre with a line of grips. Repeat this on the opposite side, then comb the back section up and push in a line of grips just below the crown area. For extra support, push in a couple of glitzy hair combs.

◀ Make a side parting then gather up one side of your hair and twist it loosely down to the nape. Repeat on the other side. Secure the hair with a covered elastic band and decorate with a bright bow. Finger-comb your curls or use a tail comb to help them spread out to form a full ponytail at the back.

TRICKS — of the trade
STYLING TOOLS

● **Heated styling tools:** these are your greatest aid for straightening or altering the shape of your curls.

● **Straightening irons:** these have two flat plates between which you sandwich sections of hair. You then pull the straighteners smoothly to the ends of the section in one movement. If your hair is very curly, they work best after you have blow-dried most of the curl out of your hair.

● **Blow-dryer:** use the styling nozzle on your hairdryer to concentrate the hot air on individual strands to smooth hair down. For soft, rippling waves, finger-comb your hair as you blow-dry. Or

curl your hair round a styling brush for an extra sleek finish.

● **Crimpers:** these have twin hotplates between which you sandwich your hair. The plates are rippled to produce a wavy finish.

● **Tongs:** these produce tight ringlets that can stay in place until you wash your hair. They're also excellent for smoothing down frizz – simply apply styling spray and tong frizzy sections into uniform curls or loose waves.

WATCHPOINTS

● Don't weigh down your curls by applying heavy styling products, or make hair even frizzier by using one that has a drying effect. Try using one of the special made-for-curl mousses recommended for permed hair, as these are very lightweight. Or try a curl-reviving spray for bouncy curls, or a volume-building spray to add extra body.

● Drying your hair vigorously with a towel will rough up the cuticle and make curly hair look dull and frizzy. Instead, pat away excess moisture and leave hair to dry naturally, or use an infra-red lamp, diffuser, or wrap your hair in a towel until it's completely dry.

61

HAIR STYLING PROJECT 11: CURLY HAIR VARIATIONS

RESTYLING CURLY HAIR

1 Work a blob of styling mousse through from the roots to the ends. If your hair is very curly, first blow-dry it straight. Then wind sections of hair on to rollers. Use the largest rollers at the front and on top where you want the least curl.

tip Make sure you don't use heated rollers unless your hair is dry.

PREPARATION

TIME about 45 minutes

HAVE TO HAND
● blow-dryer ● styling brush ● heated rollers ● mousse ● hair spray ● Afro comb

2 Wait until the rollers have cooled down, then take them out in the order you put them in, being careful not to pull out the curls. Brush your hair through gently. Use an Afro comb to tease out the ends into soft waves. Spritz with a light mist of hairspray to hold the style in place.

PROBLEM
•SOLVER•

PERMING TO CONTROL CURLS

Recommending a perm to someone with curly hair may seem strange but it can help control curls.

● Hair is often curly in one place and almost straight in others. If you want to even up the curl, you can have selected areas permed. As this can be fairly tricky, don't attempt it yourself at home – talk to your hairdresser who can advise if it's right for your particular type of hair.

● When you are looking for a long-term solution to frizzy hair, perming could be the answer. It can create a variety of curls, and as it has natural body and wave, you will be less likely to have unattractive flat roots when the perm starts to grow out.

● Very curly or Afro hair can be straightened using a special type pf perms available at salons. But remember that perming solutions are hard on hair, so only consider it if your hair is in good condition.

● If you are having your hair permed and coloured, the perm should be done at least a week before colouring.

62

• TECHNIQUE 13 •
USING HENNA

Change your image by changing your hair colour using one of the oldest colourants around – henna. This natural product can not only give your hair a complete colour change, but it also adds shine and leaves your hair in superb condition. Follow this week's Technique and learn how to apply henna with the minimum of fuss for fabulous results.

PREPARATION

TIME *45 minutes – 2½ hours, depending on desired colour strength*

HAVE TO HAND
• comb • butterfly grips • glass mixing bowl • henna powder • plastic spoon • cling film/shower cap • old towel • cotton wool • petroleum jelly/cold cream • plastic gloves • mild shampoo • hairdryer

1 ◀◀◀◀ ◀◀◀ ◀◀
Shampoo your hair to remove the natural hair oil, which would form a barrier against the henna. Towel-dry your hair and divide it into four sections. Secure each section with a butterfly grip. Put the henna powder in a glass mixing bowl and add boiling water. Use a plastic spoon to mix the henna powder into a smooth paste.

 tip *For a subtle colour result, add a touch more water but for stronger results, make the paste thicker.*

63

2 ▲▲▲▲▲▲▲

Use your fingertips to apply a thick layer of petroleum jelly or cold cream round your hairline and over your ears. This protects the skin from the henna paste and helps stop it becoming stained.

⭐ *tip* *Make sure the petroleum jelly or cold cream doesn't cover any of your hair or it will stop the henna working.*

B·R·E·A·K·I·N·G THE CODE

There are many myths surrounding henna and what it can do, so check our code-breaking guide to find out the truth:

- Henna works primarily by wrapping itself round the individual hair shafts. Unlike chemical tints, henna doesn't penetrate deep into the hair itself.
- Many henna products claim to give your hair extra body. This is because of henna's wrapping action which gives a fuller look to each hair shaft.
- Henna is a superb conditioner but only when used occasionally. Continual reapplication can damage the hair and make it dull.
- There are lots of henna-related products available. Shampoos and conditioners containing a small quantity of henna won't tint your hair, but will help prevent it fading. And henna conditioning waxes help make your hair soft by moisturising the hair cuticles.

Colour test

To check how the henna is taking, pull out a few strands from under the cling film and rub the hair strands dry. If the colour isn't strong enough, put more henna on the dried strands and perform the test again later. Red henna is a popular colour and here's a guideline to the results it will have on your natural hair colour.

COLOUR CHART

NATURAL HAIR COLOUR	DEVELOPMENT TIME	RESULT
Golden brown	1/2-1hr	auburn
Light brown	1/2-1hr	auburn
Mid-brown	1-4hrs	chestnut
Dark brown	1-4hrs	chestnut
Black	2-6hrs	red highlights

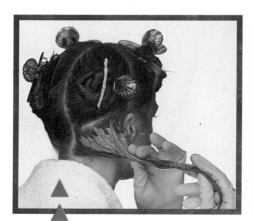

3 ▲▲▲▲▲▲▲▲▲

Wear an old towel over your shoulders to protect your clothing. Starting on the lower layers at the nape of the neck, divide off a 2.5cm (1in) layer of hair. Put on your plastic gloves, then smooth a generous blob of henna down the hair strands. Don't worry about leaving the roots henna free – you can coat them later. Leave the top layers and fringe until last – these upper layers tend to be drier than the rest of your hair and so take the henna colour more quickly.

4 ▲▲▲▲▲▲▲

When you are sure that you've achieved complete and even coverage, use your fingertips to massage the henna into your roots.

⭐ *tip* *Although it's possible to henna your hair on your own (one large mirror placed behind and one in front of you to give an all-round view will help), you'll find it easiest if you ask a friend to help.*

5 ▲▲▲▲▲▲▲▲

Cover your hair with cling film or a plastic shower cap to keep your scalp warm and so help the colour to develop. To check how the colour is taking, perform the colour test described above. When the colour has developed, remove the cling film and rinse your hair with warm water. Then shampoo as usual.

⭐ *tip* *Speed up the process by applying heat to your scalp with a hairdryer.*

HAIR STYLING TECHNIQUE 13: USING HENNA

• PROJECT 12 •

RETOUCHING YOUR ROOTS

Successful colouring with henna is relatively easy on hair that hasn't been dyed before, but as the roots start to grow out, the problems begin. Follow Project 12 and learn how to retouch your roots without affecting the rest of your hair, so you'll keep an even all-over cover.

PREPARATION

TIME *30 minutes – 2$\frac{1}{2}$ hours*

HAVE TO HAND
- henna powder • plastic spoon
- mixing bowl • tinting brush
- old towel

Divide your dry hair with a centre parting. Use a tinting brush to paint henna as close to your roots as possible, without actually colouring your skin.

tip Make the henna paste as thick as you can, to prevent the henna dripping on to already tinted hair.

Did you know...?

- Henna is made from the powdered leaves of Egyptian privet. It is a natural colourant containing no manufactured chemicals.
- Henna has been used for thousands of years to dye hair and, in some cultures, even skin.
- You can buy henna powders that have had other natural ingredients added to produce a variety of colour shades from golden brown to black.
- The effects of henna can last for between three to four months and the colour fades with time. If you've had a perm or your hair is very dry, the colour will be stronger than it would be on hair that's in good condition before you start.

65

2 Going from the back of your head to the front, use the end of the henna brush or a tail comb to part the hair into 12mm (¹/₂in) sections. Working a section at a time, paint the roots on the underside of the section, and the top of the section below, until all your hair roots are fully covered in henna.

PROBLEM •SOLVER•

Applying henna is a messy business. Protect yourself and your clothes by following these simple steps:
• Use cold cream or petroleum jelly to protect your hairline, and place a strip of cotton wool across your forehead to stop the henna dripping on to your face and neck.

• Henna can discolour fabrics, so make sure your clothes are well-protected by wrapping an old towel around your shoulders, or wearing an old T-shirt, which you don't mind spoiling.
• Wear rubber gloves while rinsing your hair as even minimal contact with henna can stain your hands.

ATCHPOINTS

• Don't use henna if your hair is more than 20 per cent grey. Grey hairs tend to be very porous and turn bright orange!
• Don't use henna if you have very dry hair, the ends of your hair will be more porous than the rest of your hair and you could end up with an uneven result.
• Don't henna your hair just before having a perm, as henna forms a barrier against perming chemicals.
• Don't use henna if you have peroxide blonde hair as it will turn your hair orange.
• Don't use henna if your hair has been colour treated recently.

3 Push your hair off your forehead – the henna's thick consistency will hold the hair back. Allow the colour time to develop, perform the colour test described in Technique 13 and then rinse off the henna.

tip Use a hairdryer to speed up processing, but protect your hair length from heat damage by dampening it down.

Suit yourself

An at-a-glance guide to the different henna colours available on the market.

HENNA COLOURS
Usually henna produces brown or red colour shades, but it can be added to other natural ingredients to create a wider range of colours, from golden brown to black.
Dark brown/black henna – this henna powder is made from henna leaves, a herb called catechu and dried walnut leaves. It produces a dark brown colour on most hair tones, and can take between one and six hours to develop.

Red-brown henna – henna powder is mixed with rich brown Turkish coffee and indigo plant extracts. Mid-brown hair shades turn a rich chestnut colour. It takes between one and four hours to develop, depending on how strong you want the colour to be.
Blonde henna – henna powder is combined with chamomile flowers and rhubarb root. Apply lemon juice to your hair during the colour development, as the citric acid helps lighten the tone.

Blonde henna gives golden highlights to light brown or fair hair.
Henna treatment wax – contains no trace of a tint but simply smooths and moisturises the hair cuticles. Apply regularly to permed or colour treated hair to restore it to a healthy condition. The treatment works best in warm, damp conditions, so either apply henna treatment wax while you are having a steamy bath, or wrap your hair in a warm, damp towel for 20-30 minutes.

• TECHNIQUE 14 •

CHOOSING THE RIGHT HAIRSTYLE

*face
shape
Hair type
un solo
Titulo*

A good hairstyle should flatter your face shape, make the most of your best features and suit the texture of your hair. Find out how to choose the hairstyle that's right for you – before you go for the chop – with the help of Technique 14.

LONG FACE

When your face is longer than it is wide, with your forehead, cheekbones and jaw of roughly equal width, you fall into this category. Your aim should be visually to reduce the length and increase the width of your face.

STYLE SUGGESTIONS
● *Make a thin face appear wider by styling any shorter top layers by back-combing then smoothing into place. Leave longer layers to flare out at the ends.*

● *A short layered style with a textured fringe appears to shorten the length of the face. The layers can be styled for maximum width by gently scrunch drying.*
● *A heavy fringe is the easiest way to shorten a long face.*
● *Avoid too much root lift and concentrate on adding width.*

TRICKS — —of the trade

ASSESSING YOUR FACE SHAPE

Although faces fall into the general categories that are mentioned here, you may not find it easy to identify your face shape. If you're not sure which group you belong to, try this simple test. Sit in front of a mirror and fasten your hair back to reveal your hairline – your face shape will instantly seem clearer. Then tape a piece of fine tissue paper to the mirror and draw round the outline of your face as reflected in the mirror. Remove the tissue paper, then check which face shape the outline matches.

67

OVAL FACE

Oval faces are rounded at the top, have strong cheekbones, and gradually narrow down to the chin. This is a well balanced face shape, and the easiest one for which to find a hairstyle. The balance, however, can be tipped by a prominent feature such as a large nose but, in general, oval faces suit extremes of style as well as classic cuts. Blunt fringes, asymmetric cuts, strongly textured or sculptured shapes and hair drawn sleekly off the face are all good options.

STYLE SUGGESTIONS

● *Long, straight, one-length hair often looks good with a blunt-cut fringe. Alternatively, go for an angled cut.*

● *A short, textured cut with plenty of root lift, will flatter a well-balanced oval face.*

● *Choose styles that feature extreme contrasts of shape and texture, such as a short bob with graduated ends.*

PROBLEM
• SOLVER •

LARGE EARS

If they're large and stick out, camouflage them with long textured hair or curls.

Opt for: Full layers, a curly perm or waves.

Avoid: Very short cuts, dead straight hair and putting your hair up.

PROMINENT NOSE

Select styles that draw attention away from the nose and balance out your features.

Opt for: Soft, textured looks, side partings, or a textured fringe, styled for height.

Avoid: Hair drawn tightly off the face, blunt fringes, and centre partings that connect with the line of the nose.

SHORT NECK

Don't hide your neck under masses of hair – instead select styles that lengthen it.

Opt for: Hair cut short at the nape of the neck to lengthen it visually. Dress your hair up to lead your eye upwards.

Avoid: Shoulder-length

textured looks that cover the neck.

HIGH FOREHEAD

Aim to reduce the length and bulk of your forehead.

Opt for: Heavy blunt fringes or slightly textured versions, which will lighten the forehead.

LOW FOREHEAD

Style your hair cleverly to add height at the forehead.

Opt for: Soft fringes that start several inches behind your hairline, styles with height at the front, and wear your hair up and pinned back off your forehead, to create height on top.

Avoid: Heavy blunt fringes.

SMALL EYES

Make sure your hair doesn't flop over your eyes, making them look smaller.

Opt for: Hair taken away from the face or light, face-framing shapes.

Avoid: Heavy fringes and hair that falls forwards.

ROUND FACE

Round faces are more than three-quarters the length of the face at their widest point. The cheekbones tend to be very wide and the chin weak. Any of the hairstyles below should appear to slim down the wide features and lengthen the face.

STYLE SUGGESTIONS

● *If your hair's short, bring tendrils of hair forwards on to the face. Balance these with a light, textured fringe, which allows your forehead to show through so that you don't shorten your face.*

● *Long hair that's slightly layered and brushed forwards on to the face has a slimming effect.*

● *Lengthen facial proportions by piling curls high on top of your head. Narrow your face by drawing your hair back at the sides.*

HAIR STYLING TECHNIQUE 14: CHOOSING THE RIGHT HAIRSTYLE

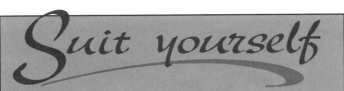

Suit yourself

An at-a-glance chart to choose the best style for your hair type.

FINE

Characteristics

Soft, flyaway hair. Easily damaged by heat/chemical processing and doesn't hold the shape created by heat styling for more than a few hours.

Styling tips

● Invest in a good haircut.
● Avoid too much heat styling/chemical processing.
● Use lightweight styling products like mousses, and choose shampoos/conditioners with ingredients that promote volume. Avoid heavy cream conditioners.
● Use hairspray to control flyaway hair.

FINE / THIN

Characteristics

Similar characteristics to fine hair but less of it.

Styling tips

● Opt for blunt one-length styles that make hair appear thicker.
● Perms can make well-conditioned hair appear fuller.
● Avoid styles that lift the hair too much on top as you could have see-through areas.
● Use shampoos, conditioners and styling products specially formulated to add extra body.

FINE / THICK

Characteristics

Same characteristics as fine hair but there is a lot more of it. This hair type can be oily as more hair follicles mean more oil-producing sebaceous glands. Hair tends to be limp and flat and static can be a problem.

Styling tips

● Layers can lessen the hair's weight and give your hair a natural bounce.

● One-length styles that show off naturally straight, shiny hair and don't require root lift are ideal.
● A perm can be useful but it may drop out quickly – if your hair doesn't hold curl well when you style it, it may well flop when curls are permed in.
● Colour, especially highlights, is a good way to liven up the hair.
● Always use conditioner to prevent static build up, but make sure it's a lightweight spray.

FINE / CURLY

Characteristics

A manageable, attractive hair type, but its abundance of curl can disguise the fact that it's just as delicate as other fine hair. Overworking with heat stylers can lead to frizz, especially if you have a fine fringe.

Styling tips

Choose layers for maximum curl or one-length cuts to relax over-tight curls. Avoid too much heat styling, which can make curls frizz, and condition regularly with a leave-in spray.

MEDIUM

Characteristics

Typically mid-European hair of a medium texture and shade. It's relatively easy to style and holds the shape of a cut well.

Styling tips

● Don't over-use heated styling tools as this hair type can quickly lose its condition.
● Make sure the hair is in tip-top condition before considering a perm or colour treatment.
● Pay careful attention to conditioning at all times – condition after every shampoo and have regular trims.

SQUARE FACE

The forehead, cheekbones and jaw are of roughly equal width and are accompanied by a square jaw.

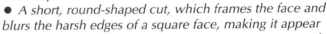

STYLE SUGGESTIONS

● A soft style balances a hard square jaw. Back-comb the hair at the front to add root lift and visually lengthen the square face shape.
● A short, round-shaped cut, which frames the face and blurs the harsh edges of a square face, making it appear more oval.
● A textured style is useful for softening a square jawline, while graduated layers give a wide, fairly high outline that tends to draw attention away from the jaw.

WATCHPOINTS

Think carefully before you commit yourself to a particular style as you must be prepared to spend the time, effort and money necessary to maintain the look. Ask your hairdresser's advice – if you've chosen a look that opposes your hair's natural texture (such as a perm on straight hair or a sleek look on hair with a natural kink), they'll guide you on the practicality of your choice and tell you how often you'll need to return to the salon. They can also advise you on the best styling products for your hair type.

Suit yourself

It is important to take into account the texture of your hair when choosing a hairstyle. To discover which category your hair fits in to, consult the handy chart below.

THICK / COARSE

Characteristics

Prevalent in Oriental races and people with dark – but not Afro – hair. Individual hairs are bulky and have a coarse texture.

Styling tips

● Styling potential is great as this type of hair can take a lot of punishment. But don't overdo it and condition regularly.

● If thick or coarse hair does lose condition, curlier hair tends to frizz while straighter hair goes limp.

● Avoid chemical treatments, such as colourants or perms. When dry, this hair type absorbs perm chemicals quickly, but the natural weight can make the curls drop out. When well conditioned, perm and colour chemicals take a long time to penetrate the hair shaft and so cause damage.

AFRO

Characteristics

A tightly curled hair type with uneven curls. The hair's natural curl gives the illusion of thickness but this hair type can be delicate and dry.

Styling tips

● Chemical straightening can smooth out and control frizz, but this should only really be done at a salon.

● Perms can even out the curl texture if hair's in good enough condition.

● Make the most of the hair's potential for sculpted and woven shapes.

● Pay extra attention to condition.

DRY / FRIZZY

Characteristics

Some of the above hair types can become dry and frizzy – when curly, the hair flares into a mass of frizz, making it unmanageable. Heat and humidity also make the hair shafts swell and stick up.

Styling tips

● Treat yourself to regular trims to remove dry, frizzy ends.

● Condition with rich creams and apply leave-in conditioning sprays to help smooth the frizz.

● Try setting hair on rollers to help straighten it.

● Avoid using heated styling tools. Instead, use moisturising styling products, such as wax and moulding cream, to slick the hair into shape.

DRY / LIMP

Characteristics

A naturally dry scalp or over-processing/excess exposure to heat can dry out hair, making it floppy and unmanageable.

Styling tips

● Avoid perms and heated styling tools

● Condition regularly and use mild shampoos to avoid stripping hair of moisture.

OILY

Characteristics

Active sebaceous glands lead to oily hair, which makes hair limp and hard to style. If oily hair is long, it is often accompanied by dry ends.

Styling tips

● Wash hair frequently with a mild shampoo – strong shampoo clears grease by stripping away natural oils, but it also stimulates the glands and makes them step up oil prodcution.

HEART-SHAPED FACE

STYLE SUGGESTIONS

● *Short hair slicked back at the sides and styled in a quiff at the front emphasises a heart-shaped face, making the most of its delicate proportions.*

Wide cheekbones and forehead contrast with a small and slightly pointed chin to form a classic heart shape. This This can be exaggerated further by a widow's peak hairline. At its best, the shape can be very attractive, but you may need to minimise the width at the cheeks to create a better balance.

● *Conceal an extra wide forehead with a light, curly fringe. Alternatively, balance a small chin with spiral-curled one-length hair.*

● *A heart-shaped face that's fairly wide at the temples can be disguised by styling hair forwards to cover the temple area. Hair layers are shaped for width and height but styled gently forwards to hide the temples without covering the whole forehead.*

HAIR STYLING TECHNIQUE 14: CHOOSING THE RIGHT HAIRSTYLE

• PROJECT 13 •

ADDING WIDTH

A wide style can balance the shape of your face and make your hair look fuller. So in Project 13 we've widened a one-length bob, both at the ends and higher up at the roots, to produce a selection of looks that could be right for you.

PREPARATION

TIME 20 minutes

HAVE TO HAND
- butterfly combs • hairdryer • styling brush
- vent brush • fine comb • styling spray

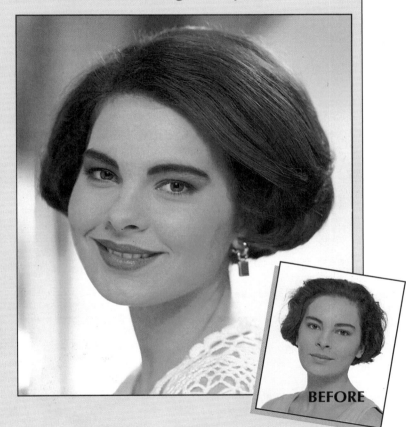

1 Wash and towel-dry your hair, then divide it into sections with buttefly combs. Blow-dry one small section of hair at a time, paying particular attention to the roots as you dry, to give them as much lift as possible. Use a vent brush to draw each section upwards and dry each layer from underneath, taking the hairdryer as close to the roots as possible without burning your scalp.

BEFORE

2 Use a fine-toothed comb to backcomb your hair at the roots to help your hair stand away from the scalp – ruffling the hair's cuticles in this way makes it coarser and more likely to stand out from the scalp.

tip Concentrate most of your back-combing efforts on the lower layers – these support the top layers and so increase the width of the style rather than the height.

3 Tilt your head and apply a fine mist of hairspray to hold the lower layers in place. Wait a few seconds for it to dry before lifting your head up.

tip Don't brush or comb your hair at this stage, as it will flatten out the volume you've added. Instead, draw a comb along the surface hair only, without digging the teeth into the bulk of the hairstyle.

71

CURLY HAIR

1 Set a one-length bob on heated rollers to add width at the temple area and make the hair appear layered – the curls make the hair seem shorter at the nape of the neck, but lift hair into a high, wide style elsewhere.

2 Allow the rollers to cool down then take them out and loosen the curls by gently combing them through with your fingers.

★ *tip* *Mist the finished style with hairspray.*

Hairbands

• When your hair is straight it has a natural tendency to flatten out and width can be hard to maintain. Accessories that hold your style in place could be the answer.
• Use a simple hairband to emphasise a wide shape. Slide the band on to your hair and push back to several centimetres behind your hairline. Your hair will naturally flare out around the band.

Swept-over look

• Add width to one side only with this glamorous look. Use a comb to draw hair back on one side and carry it round to the other side. Spray with hairspray to smooth it down and hold it in place. The contrast between the two sides will make your hair appear fuller.

TRICKS — — of the trade

HOW TO BALANCE YOUR FACE SHAPE

• *Long face – extra width counteracts the length of your face and makes it appear wider.*
• *Slim face – extra width balances your head with your body.*

• *Square face – if the width is concentrated high up it will create an inverted triangle, minimising a strong, square jaw.*
• *Heart-shaped face – create width then allow a little hair to fall on to the temples.*
• *Round face – avoid adding width as it will only make your face look plumper.*
• *Strong cheekbones – width will emphasise your fine cheekbones.*

Suit yourself

Different types and styles of hair need individual attention , so use this at-a-glance chart as your styling guide.

LAYERED CURLS
Scrunch dry your hair with a diffuser to increase its width, but avoid creating too much root lift on top as this will give a round look to your style rather than making it look wider.

ONE-LENGTH CURLS
The weight of the hair will pull it down at the roots, so add width concentrating styling efforts at the sides and the hair ends. Fingercomb the sides outwards and upwards, directing your dryer underneath for maximum lift. Scrunch ends tightly in the palms of your hands to give the curls a boost.

SHORT LAYERS
Apply a firm-hold hair gel to lower layers of hair at the back and sides of your head. Blow-dry your hair upside-down using your fingers as a comb to direct the hair strands upwards and

outwards. Add wax to the top layers to add texture – wax blends with the textured look of the under sections without creating too much root lift.

SHORT, ONE-LENGTH HAIR
Blow-dry a graduated cut with longer layers on top section by section. Dry the hair from underneath, to help make the top hair stand out.

LONG HAIR
Pile your hair up on top to add width. Try a cottage loaf bun with soft tendrils falling around your hairline; twist bunches into coiled knots at either side; or use accessories to draw attention to the side sections.

LONG LAYERED HAIR
Scrunch dry your hair to increase it's width, or try rolling it loosely at the sides and pinning it into place. Alternatively, set it in rollers and spray it with hairspray.

• TECHNIQUE 15 •

HAIRDRYER GUIDE

When your hair just won't go the right way, it could be your hairdryer that's at fault. There are so many different kinds on the market that buying the wrong one is an all-too-common mistake. So in this issue we help you choose and use the hairdryer that's right for you.

◄ PROFESSIONAL DRYER

Based on those used in salons, this is a large, powerful dryer (1200 to 2000 watts) with a long, thin cylindrical barrel. It has a selection of heat/speed settings and a number of attachments that fit over the barrel.

INFRA-RED ▼

The hair is dried under hot lamps which encourage curl and reduce the chance of heat damage. Salons use octopus-style infra-red lamps to dry perms and speed up colour treatments. For home use, you can buy a mini infra-lamp.

STANDARD DRYER ►

This lightweight blow-dryer has 1000 to 2000 watts of power and two heat/speed settings. All models feature a clip-on concentrator nozzle, and some are available with a diffuser.

▼ HOT AIRBRUSH DRYER

Based on a hotbrush design, the barrel has small holes through which warm air is blown. Easy-to-use, it works as a brush and a hairdryer. Plus the heat/speed level is low, so it's ideal for stopping frizz without over-exposing hair to strong heat. Airbrush dryers are also good for curling hair ends and adding root lift.

HAIR STYLING

DIFFUSER

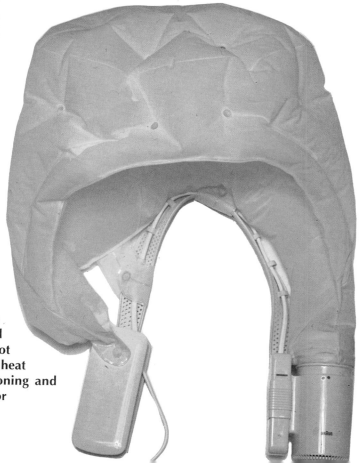

These bowl-shaped attachments are designed to dry hair gently and slowly, and are used to build in body and curl. They are available separately, but don't fit all models of hairdryer, so check they fit yours before you part with your money.

TRAVEL DRYER

This scaled-down version of the standard dryer is light and handy for travel. Most models have a fold-away handle, and power usually ranges from 1000 to 1200 watts, with dual voltage for worldwide use.

HOOD DRYER

A hood unit fits over the head and dries hair at a gentle speed. Some are available with a stand, like a traditional salon dryer, while others are portable sacks that fill with hot air. Heat/speed settings are low so hair is protected from heat damage. Hood dryers are suitable for intensive conditioning and colour treatments that require heat to activate them, and for setting hair on rollers.

Suit yourself

Different hair types require different dryers. Although some can be used for a number of looks, others have more specific functions. Find out which is right for you.

LONG/THICK HAIR

This hair type is slow-drying so it requires a powerful dryer. Choose a professional dryer or high-powered standard dryer with all available attachments.

LONG/FINE HAIR

Can become flyaway or tangled. Use a professional or standard dryer on a low heat/speed setting. If your hair has natural or permed curls, a diffuser or infra-red dryer is useful.

WAVY/CURLY HAIR

A dryer with diffuser or infra-red lamp will encourage body and curl. If you haven't got a diffuser, use a standard dryer to rough-dry your hair.

MID-LENGTH HAIR

Use a professional or standard dryer for basic styling. A hood dryer is useful for set looks and for adding body while maintaining a smooth finish. If you want to add a bit of shape to your hair, a hot brush can be used for gentle styling.

SHORT HAIR

Use a standard dryer on a medium setting as a strong heat can dry out the hair. Use the concentrator nozzle to lift the roots. Hood dryers and hot brushes will help set the style. For styling away from home, a cordless hotbrush or a travel dryer can produce some excellent results.

74

HAIR STYLING TECHNIQUE 15

• PROJECT 14 •

DRYING METHODS

How you use your hairdryer is just as important as the model you choose. Follow Project 14 and discover a number of ways to achieve the look that's perfect for you.

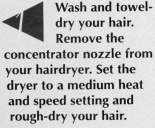

BEFORE

PREPARATION

TIME *15-20 minutes, depending on hair's thickness.*

HAVE TO HAND
Equipment – • hairdryer with concentrator nozzle • mousse • butterfly grips • styling brush • vent brush • water/ conditioning spray

BLOW DRYING

◀ Wash and towel-dry your hair. Remove the concentrator nozzle from your hairdryer. Set the dryer to a medium heat and speed setting and rough-dry your hair.

tip *Make sure the air reaches the roots by agitating your hair with your fingertips - this separates out the strands, exposing the root area.*

▶ While hair is still damp, divide it into sections. Sleek blow-dried hair requires precision drying, and sectioning helps you to work on specific areas without other hair getting in the way. It also prevents damp hair touching dry areas, altering their styled shape.

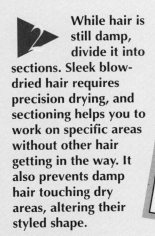

tip *Use butterfly clips rather than hair grips to hold large sections of hair.*

75

3 Start blow drying the hair at the nape of the neck, moving up the sides and top layers to the crown. Wind the hair on to a standard styling brush and dry from the roots to the ends, pulling the hair strands taut. If your hair's thick, use a vent brush to help speed up drying.

tip Direct hot air down the hair shaft to smooth down the cuticles and make your hair shine.

4 Leave styling the front sections of hair until last. Hair at the fringe is often finer than hair at the crown or nape, and is often dried out by over styling. If this is the case, dampen the hair with leave-in conditioner, and use your dryer on the lowest setting.

PROBLEM •SOLVER•

Heat can dry out your hair so follow these tips to minimise the damage.
• Reduce the time the hair strands come into contact with heat by moving your dryer from side to side.
• Make sure the concentrator nozzle doesn't come into direct contact with your hair strands – keep it a few inches away as you dry.
• Don't let sections of hair dry out too much before you work on them or they'll be difficult to style and vulnerable to heat damage. Keep a water spray or conditioner spray handy to dampen down sections of hair before styling.

TRICKS —of the trade

ROOT DIRECTION
• Although blow-drying creates a sleek finish, the volume you achieve depends on how you style the roots. To smooth the hair down at the roots, use a styling brush to pull hair down as you dry.
• For extra volume at the roots, use a brush to pull hair outwards.
• For maximum width and height, pull sections of hair upwards and direct the hairdryer at the roots from below. Use a vent brush to lift the hair gently but firmly upwards.

AIRBRUSH DRYING

Follow our standard blow-drying technique to smooth down your hair. Dampen down the ends of your hair and the hair at the nape of the neck with a light mist of styling spray. Wind the ends of your hair outwards around your airbrush styler, and hold in place until dry.

tip If you have a fringe, style it over your airbrush to create a soft wave to match your flicked ends. If not, wind hair roots backwards around the styler, pulling gently upwards as the hair dries to give added height.

SCRUNCH DRYING

PREPARATION

TIME *10-15 minutes, depending on hair's thickness.*

HAVE TO HAND
Equipment – ● hairdryer with a diffuser attachment
● natural-hold mousse ● butterfly clips

Did you know...?

Hair can become tired and over-stressed by being worked too hard with heated styling appliances. As well as damaging the hair condition, particularly at its vulnerable ends, it will leave your style limp. Dry hair shafts also stimulate sebaceous glands to produce more oil. This is intended to moisturise and protect your scalp hair, but will also make it limp and greasy. To solve the problem, keep your heat styling to a minimum (that includes other tools like tongs, heated rollers as well as dryers), and investigate other styling methods such as natural drying, setting with cold rollers and shaping with styling products.

1 Work a blob of mousse through damp hair, then divide it into sections, leaving a few inches loose at the nape of the neck if this area is too short for scrunching. Tilt your head forwards and use your fingers to comb the hair at the nape upwards for maximum volume.

tip Attach the concentrator nozzle to your hairdryer to focus hot air on the roots.

2 Remove the concentrator nozzle and attach a diffuser to your hairdryer. Take out the butterfly clips so that you can work on your whole head of hair. Use your fingers to lift the roots, scrunching them lightly in the palms of your hands as you dry.

3 To dry the hair ends, screw up a handful of hair in your fist. Allow the air to pass through the gaps in your fingers. Hold each scrunched section for a count of five, then move on to the next section.

tip A tight handful of hair produces stronger waves while a looser handful gives softness and volume.

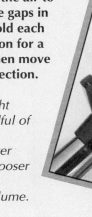

WATCHPOINTS

● Air filters at the back of the barrel should never be blocked or the dryer may overheat – take off the filter cover regularly to remove any dust build-up. Turn off your dryer if you smell burning.
● Wash off any styling products that are stuck to your dryer or its attachments.

B·R·E·A·K·I·N·G
THE CODE

Professional hairdressers use a variety of drying method to create different finishes. Check our simple glossary to find out just what can be done and the products you'll need to help you do it.

BLOW-DRYING

This basic drying method achieves a smooth, straight finish. Use a powerful hairdryer and attach a concentrator nozzle for maximum smoothing action. Hold the hair strands taut with a styling brush as you dry, or use your fingers as a comb for a softer, fuller look. Products to use: mousse, gel, styling spray, styling cream, leave-in conditioning spray or setting lotion.

GRIP DRYING

Divide your hair into sections and twist each section between the fingers as you blow-dry. This creates curls which can be strong or loose depending how tight you twist the hair strands and how large a section you twist. Products to use: mousse, gel, styling cream.

HOOD DRYING

Rough dry your hair, apply a styling product, then wind your hair in rollers. Place the hood dryer over your hair and turn it to a warm setting. To cool the curls, switch the dryer on to a low setting. Products to use: mousse, setting lotion.

RUB DRYING

Use the palms of your hands to create root lift on top. Rub your hand along your scalp in circular movements as you dry. Products to use: light-hold mousse and styling cream.

FINGER-DRYING

Any drying method that uses your fingers as a tool to shape your hair. Also a method of drying short to mid-length hair without a dryer – you simply shape and comb your hair into place with your fingers as it dries. Products to use: mousse, gel, wet-look gel, wax, styling cream.

INFRA-RED DRYING

Sit under the lamp, switch it on and just wait for your hair to dry. Don't try to speed up the process by sitting nearer the lamp – infra-red may cause less heat damage than any other dryer, but if the hair ends come into contact with the lamp over a prolonged period, they could dry out. Products to use: conditioning spray, light-hold mousse.

NATURAL DRYING

Any method which doesn't involve a styling tool, such as a hairdryer, and requires only minimal shaping using brushes, combs or your hands. Hair can be left to dry naturally, or it can have a product worked through it before it is brushed or combed into shape. Products to use: wet gel or styling wax, mousse, conditioning spray or moulding cream.

ROUGH DRYING

A basic method where you aim the dryer at your hair and agitate hair with your fingers to speed up drying and encourage volume. This can be a

drying technique in itself, or simply used to remove excess moisture. Products to use: mousse, conditioning spray, gel, styling cream.

WAVING

Use the palms of your hands to create wave shapes as you blow-dry. For soft waves, weave sections of hair between your fingers and direct the hot air at them. For a waved peak fringe area, draw hair tightly back at the front using the flat of your hand. Rest your little finger two or three inches behind your hairline, then push your hair forwards so it forms a peak, and dry. Products to use: strong-hold mousse, gel, styling cream, styling spray, wax.

SCRUNCH DRYING

Scrunch a handful of hair in your fist to produce curl or volume. This technique is ideal for curly or layered hair. When your hair is dry, apply a small amount of styling product and work it in with your fingers from the roots to the ends. Products to use: mousse, natural-hold gel, wax, styling cream.

TOWEL DRYING

Removes excess moisture before using another styling method. Don't rub your hair with the towel as this reduces shine. Simply take sections of hair and squeeze your towel around them to absorb water. Towel dry your hair before applying any styling product.

HAIR STYLING PROJECT 14: DRYING METHODS

• TECHNIQUE 16 •

STYLING LAYERED HAIR

A layered cut can be one of the most versatile to style once you know how. In Technique 16 we show you four variations on a lightly layered style – one of them is bound to be right for you.

1 Wash and towel-dry your hair. Use your fingers to work natural-hold mousse through your hair and then rough dry to get rid of the bulk of the water, using a blow-dryer on a low setting. Divide your hair into sections and secure them with sectioning grips. Begin by blow-drying the lower sections, directing the hot air down the hair shaft. Work from the back of the head, but don't dry the sides and top layers as they need to stay damp for styling later.

tip *If the sides and top do dry, dampen with a water spray before styling.*

BEFORE

FORWARD SWEEP

PREPARATION

TIME *20 minutes.*

HAVE TO HAND
Equipment – • professional blow-dryer • sectioning grips • styling brush • water spray • gloss spray

2 Release each top section in turn from its sectioning grips and wind the hair forwards around your styling brush. Ease the brush gently forwards from the roots as you blow-dry.

3 Lightly spray the hair strands with gloss spray and finger-comb it through to prevent static build up and flyaway ends. Don't use hairspray as you want as much shine as possible.

79

SMOOTH TOP KNOT

PREPARATION

TIME *15 minutes.*

HAVE TO HAND
Equipment – • vent brush • comb
• ponytail band • hair grips • hair spray

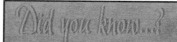

Layering describes cutting the hair to a variety of lengths without the length at the nape of the neck being affected. Layering is an ideal way to style long hair as dry ends have little chance to develop.

80

1 Brush your hair smooth and divide off the back and crown hair from behind your ears, leaving sections loose at the sides. Gather up the back hair on top of your head and secure it in a ponytail with a covered elastic band. Separate out a few strands from the back of the ponytail, wrap them around the band to hide it, and secure with hair grips.

tip *Alternatively, fasten the ponytail with a bright scrunchie band.*

2 Using a comb, back-comb your ponytail to make it appear thicker. Pay special attention to the lower layers as this will help give fine hair height and holding power.

tip *The action of back-combing ruffles the hair cuticle and detracts from the shine, so always back-comb the lower layers so that the surface remains glossy.*

3 Divide your ponytail into small sections and roll each section under, securing the ends in place with hair grips. Work from one side of the tail around the back and on to the other side, so you form a loose bun.

tip *For a smooth finish, draw your comb lightly across the surface of the bun to smooth together the hair sections.*

4 Comb the loose hair at the side so that it's smooth, and then draw it back and pin it behind your bun. Leave a few tendrils of hair loose at the front to soften the look.

tip *If your hair is heavily layered, gather the hair at the sides up into your ponytail. Leave the rest free to form loose strands at either side.*

HAIR STYLING TECHNIQUE 16: STYLING LAYERED HAIR

SOFT CURLS

PREPARATION

TIME 30 minutes

HAVE TO HAND
Equipment – • mousse • heated rollers • bendy rollers • hairspray

WATCHPOINTS

• Layered cuts keep their shape well and usually require fewer salon visits than short cuts, or one-length blunt cuts, which have to be very neat. Visit your hairdresser for a trim every 10 to 14 weeks, depending on how quickly your hair grows.

1 Work styling mousse through your hair, finger-combing it from the roots to the ends so that all the hair is evenly covered.

tip Choose a product with medium holding power for a natural-looking finish. Opt for natural-hold mousse or light spray gel.

2 Heat up your rollers, then wind your hair on to them in a random pattern – hold the section you're winding out from your head and keep it taut as you wind the roller down to the roots.

tip Here we used medium-sized heated rollers on the top section for softness, and bendy rollers elsewhere for stronger curl at the ends. Traditional rollers produce a smooth curl that varies in size depending on the roller width. Bendy rollers produce a small natural-looking curl.

3 Allow the hair to cool completely before you take out the heated rollers, as warm curls drop out quickly. Use your fingers to ruffle the curls into place, then set the style with hairspray.

81

HAIR STYLING TECHNIQUE 16: STYLING LAYERED HAIR

3 ▲ ▲ ▲ ▲ ▲ ▲ ▲

Secure the twisted hair at the crown with a line of grips down the length of the twisted section. Finger-comb the end of the twist and the hair at the back so that it forms a mass of curls. Set the style with hairspray.

DRESSED CURLS

PREPARATION

TIME *5 minutes.*

HAVE TO HAND
Equipment – • wide-toothed comb
• hair grips• hairspray

B·R·E·A·K·I·N·G THE CODE

BASIC LAYERING
Hair is held out at an angle and cut to roughly equal lengths. This creates a rounded, head-framing shape. It's ideal for adding root lift if your hair tends to flop, and for maintaining condition.

LONG LAYERS
These are suitable for straight or curly hair as they reduce the weight of hair on top without detracting from the one-length look. With long layers you can dress up your hair as if it had a blunt cut, as well as achieving height and volume with curled or scrunched styles.

THINNING
Thinning is suitable for increasing the manageability of thick or frizzy hair, as the layers reduce the weight and fullness at the ends. Hairdressers use scissors and razors to achieve the look, or they use special notched-blade scissors.

TAPERING
Designed for naturally curly hair that is being pulled flat by the hair's own weight. Using scissors or a razor, the length and bulk are removed from sections of hair.

1 ▲ ▲ ▲ ▲ ▲ ▲ ▲

Use your thumbs to make a parting that goes from ear to ear to separate out the top of your hair. Smooth out the section by gently combing it through.

2 ▲ ▲ ▲ ▲ ▲ ▲ ▲

Take the top section in one hand and loosely twist the hair along its length.

⭐ *tip* *Back-comb the section of hair at the roots to give lift to the finished look.*

⭐ *tip* *Don't make the twist too tight – the style works best if it's kept loose.*

• PROJECT 15 •

DAY INTO EVENING LOOKS

When you're going out from work, you probably re-do your make-up, but how often do you have time to change your hair? Project 15 shows you how to style short or long hair for daytime, then a few quick tricks to make it look just right for a night on the town.

QUICK CHANGE FOR SHORT HAIR

Even with very short hair, it is not difficult to achieve quite different daytime and evening looks. Our evening style is a natural progression from the the casual daytime look – sleeker and less tousled.

WATCHPOINTS

• Daytime hair has very different demands placed on it from those made on evening styles. Make sure your style is practical.
• Daytime looks are more likely to have to cope with weather extremes while you're travelling to and from work or going shopping, so simple styles are best.
• Even the most casual looks must be durable as you're likely to be out of the house for up to 10 hours. In general, go for styling products that give a strong, as opposed to stiff, hold.

DAYTIME

▶ To avoid making hair look dull and rigid, use natural-hold mousse. Spray a large blob on to your hand and work it evenly into your hair with your fingers. Comb through to make sure it's evenly distributed.

 Be sparing with your mousse – you can always add more, but too much could look dry and flaky.

▶ Section off the top of your hair and hold it out of the way with one large butterfly clip. Work on the lower layers first, damping them down if they dry out before you are ready. Blow-dry the hair section by section, pulling gently upwards with your brush as you direct the hot air under the roots. Then pull the section outwards and aim the hot air down the hair shaft for the maximum smoothing and straightening effect.

 When your hair has cooled completely, turn your head upside-down. Brush gently from underneath, then turn upright again and let the hair fall into place.

PREPARATION

TIME 10 minutes
HAVE TO HAND
• natural hold mousse
• vent brush
• hairdryer
• butterfly clips • comb

83

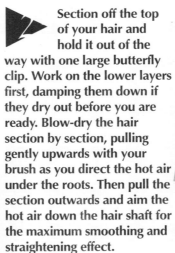

PREPARATION

TIME *10 minutes*

HAVE TO HAND
- natural hold mousse • vent brush or round brush
- hairdryer • butterfly clips • comb

EVENING

1 Work a small blob of gel through your hair, making sure it covers the crown area, as this will be the focal point of the style. Comb it through to make sure every strand has been gelled.

tip *Avoid strong, ultra-stiff gel, which can be drying and sticky. Instead, use mild, wet-look gel for a gloss finish.*

2 Lightly blow-dry the sides to fall forwards. Spray the roots with hairspray and create height on the crown by winding the hair tightly round your brush. Pull upwards as you dry, directing heat under the section and into the roots to lift the hair.

tip *To save time, wind a large roller into the crown hair – it will have the same effect as blow-drying hair round a styling brush. Leave it in while you put on your make-up.*

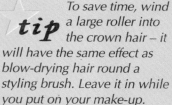
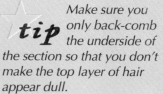

3 To make sure the root lift stays in place all evening, gently back-comb the crown hair.

tip *Make sure you only back-comb the underside of the section so that you don't make the top layer of hair appear dull.*

4 A light mist of hair spray is essential as a final back-up to your styling efforts.

tip *Use a natural-hold spray, as the stronger products can make hair stiff and may detract from its natural shine.*

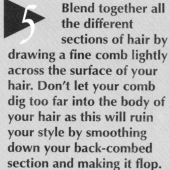

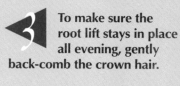

5 Blend together all the different sections of hair by drawing a fine comb lightly across the surface of your hair. Don't let your comb dig too far into the body of your hair as this will ruin your style by smoothing down your back-combed section and making it flop.

tip *A final dusting of spray will reinforce your hair's healthy shine.*

HAIR STYLING PROJECT 15: DAY INTO EVENING LOOKS

DAYTIME

2 For the quickest possible result, take large, but even, sections of hair and use small rollers. For a smooth, soft curl, as shown here, use medium-sized rollers. For a more natural-looking curl, use traditional or heated bendy rollers.

tip To wind the top area of your hair, hold it taut, vertically from your head. If your hair is very long this will be difficult, so hold the hair about halfway down the section and wind from this point to the ends. Then wind the roller down to the roots.

3 If you want to speed up the setting process, mist natural-hold hair spray lightly over your hair, then use your blow-dryer (without the concentrator nozzle) on the lowest heat/speed setting. Leave your hair to cool before you take the rollers out.

PREPARATION

TIME Winding – 10 minutes (depending on hair length and thickness). Setting – 10 to 20 minutes

HAVE TO HAND
● hairspray ● heated rollers ● setting lotion or styling spray

QUICK CHANGES FOR LONG HAIR

There are many possibilities for dressing up long hair to give it an extra glamorous look, but many of the options are complicated and time-consuming. So we've come up with a manageable as well as sophisticated evening look that's simply a straight-forward progression from our soft, daytime curls.

1 Lightly apply setting lotion or styling spray to sections of hair all over your head, making sure that you reach the underneath area. Comb it through so that all the strands of hair are evenly coated.

4 Unwind your rollers carefully, making sure that you don't pull out the curls. Don't brush your hair as this will make the curls blend into one, and could even pull them out if your hair is naturally quite straight. Instead, finger-comb your hair very gently, using your fingers to separate the curls and tease them out to their maximum volume.

tip After finger-combing, turn your head upside-down and apply hair spray. Set the spray using your hair dryer on its lowest setting.

85

EVENING

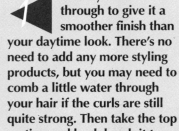

1 Brush your hair through to give it a smoother finish than your daytime look. There's no need to add any more styling products, but you may need to comb a little water through your hair if the curls are still quite strong. Then take the top section and back-brush it to give it body and a stiffer, more supportive texture.

tip *Back-brushing is just like back-combing, except of course that you use a brush! It is particularly good if your hair is very fine, or if you have a lot of hair.*

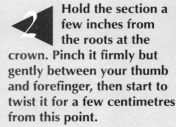

2 Hold the section a few inches from the roots at the crown. Pinch it firmly but gently between your thumb and forefinger, then start to twist it for a few centimetres from this point.

3 Keep a careful hold on the twisted section as you push the hair forwards slightly at the crown. This lifts the roots a little, creating a visible dome on top – almost like a mini beehive. Secure your hair at the crown by using a line of grips along the length of the twisted section. Your previous back-brushing should help keep the style in place, but a minimal amount of hairspray will make the shape extra secure.

tip *If your hair is heavily layered, cover the twist with a pretty hairslide or bow, which will cover up any straggly loose ends.*

PREPARATION

TIME 10 minutes
HAVE TO HAND
- water spray • brush
- hair grips
- hairslide or bow

Suit yourself

Every hairstyle has the potential to go from a daytime look to a really different finish for evening. Check our guide to find out the options.

SHORT CROPPED HAIR – Slick back using wet-look gel and twist front sections into neat kiss curls. Use styling products to produce a textured finish and to add a light finishing sheen. Use your hairdryer and mousse to change the direction of your style – sweep it forwards or direct it over to one side for an asymmetrical look.

MID-LENGTH HAIR – Use rollers or tongs for curl, or straightening irons to create a smooth finish that really shows off the shine. Try a

wash-in wash-out colourant to give depth, shine and the subtlest hint of a tint. Or experiment with fun-colour mousses, sprays and glitter.

LAYERED HAIR – Create a contrast to your daytime look by using tongs or heated rollers, or blow-dry your hair forwards for a sleeker finish.

LONG HAIR – Dress it high on your head for an sophisticated look, or leave a little hair down at the back to soften the effect.

HAIR STYLING PROJECT 15: DAY INTO EVENING LOOKS

• TECHNIQUE 17 •

DRY HAIR REPAIR

1 Wash your hair with a mild shampoo, then rinse thoroughly as shampoo residue can have a drying effect. Apply conditioner to your hair – don't skimp on the amount you use as it's important that every strand of hair is covered.

tip Comb your hair before you wash it, then gently remove any tangles after washing by easing your fingers through your hair. Don't brush your hair when it's wet either, or you risk stretching and damaging it.

Frequent use of shampoo, styling products and heated appliances has a drying effect on the hair. So Technique 17 gives you a chance to try our intensive conditioning treatment, and follow our conditioning tips to keep your hair soft and silky.

2 Taking small sections of hair, gently rub in conditioner and spread it from the roots to the ends. Continue massaging in the conditioner for at least five minutes.

tip Remember to massage conditioner into your scalp – dry hair is often accompanied by a dry scalp.

BEFORE

PREPARATION

TIME 40 minutes.

HAVE TO HAND
Equipment – • mild shampoo • intensive conditioning cream • tin foil or cling film • blow-dryer

87

3
Wrap up your treated hair in a heat-retaining material such as tin foil, cling film or a warm, damp towel. This helps speed up the action of the intensive conditioner, and prevents your wet hair from dripping on to your shoulders. Taking a bath or sitting in a hot, steamy sauna while you're treating your hair also helps the deep conditioning process.

tip *While you are allowing the intensive conditioning treatment time to work on your hair, try a deep-cleansing face mask, formulated for your skin type, or try a facial sauna.*

4
Alternatively, use a blow-dryer with a diffuser attachment to spread hot air over your hair to help boost the conditioning action. The amount of time you leave the treatment to develop depends on your hair condition: 10 minutes is enough for slightly dry hair; 20 minutes for medium-dry hair; while more serious hair damage requires 30 minutes. Rinse off the treatment after the appropriate processing time and style as usual.

tip *If a specific area of your hair is drier than the rest, apply extra conditioning treatment and concentrate the hair-dryer on that area.*

TRICKS of the trade

HOW TO TELL IF YOUR HAIR IS HEALTHY OR DRY

- *If your hair ends are lighter in colour than the rest of your hair, they're likely to be dry and should be trimmed.*
- *Brittle sections of hair dry out quickly after washing. If, by the time you come to blow-dry your hair areas have dried naturally, they need a conditioning treatment.*
- *To test if your hair is dry, take a strand of hair from your head, hold it at both ends and pull it apart very gently. Does it stretch a little before breaking or break straight away? When broken, does the end curl a little or does it stay straight? If it's dry it will break without stretching and it won't curl.*

Did you know...?

- The first hair conditioners were introduced in 1945 and were made from ingredients such as vegetable oil and eggs.
- Dark, straight hair absorbs more UVA rays than light hair, and so is more easily damaged.
- Up to 50 per cent of body heat is lost through the head.

WATCHPOINTS

To keep your hair in good condition:
- Have regular trims – the only permanent cure for dry, split ends is to have them cut off.
- Use a mild shampoo – if your scalp is flaky, don't try harsh, anti-dandruff shampoos except as a last resort. Instead, massage your scalp regularly with light oil or conditioner. And make sure you rinse your shampoo out properly, as soapy residue can contribute to scurf.
- Vary your shampoo – the combination of hard water and the continued use of the same shampoo can create a dull and drying residue on your hair.
- Limit your use of heated styling appliances as heat dries out the hair. The worst offenders are tongs, straighteners, crimpers and heated rollers, as they come into direct contact with your hair. Protect your hair from heat damage with leave-in conditioners and specially formulated styling products.
- Avoid smoky rooms – smoke draws moisture out of your hair.
- Avoid chemical processing – perming and colour treatments should only be used on hair that's in tip-top condition.
- The combination of chlorine and the sun can be very damaging, so slick hair back off your face with protective hair gel, or wear a scarf or hat for protection.
- Your hair reflects your state of health and your diet. Serious illness depletes the condition of your hair as the body conserves its energy, and the hair is the last to receive essential nutrients. As hair is made of protein, eat plenty of eggs, meat, cheese and fish.
- In winter, central heating removes moisture from the air and dries out hair. Place bowls of water next to radiators, or buy a humidifier to increase humidity levels. Or wear a hat outdoors.

SMOOTHING OUT FRIZZ

Frizz can be part of a hair's natural texture or caused by heat damage, but either way it's best treated regularly with conditioner. Try a leave-in conditioner with a liquid, rather than a cream formula, which doesn't leave a waxy film on the hair. As well as being suitable for regular conditioning, leave-in conditioners are ideal for damping down hair when restyling – and they'll protect delicate hair ends from heat damage.

1 ▶ ▶ ▶ ▶ ▶ ▶ ▶ ▶
Spray leave-in conditioner on to frizzy areas of hair and massage it in with your fingers.

2 ▶ ▶ ▶ ▶ ▶ ▶ ▶ ▶
Gently comb the conditioner all the way from the roots to the ends, then leave your hair to dry naturally or style as usual.

3 ▼ ▼ ▼ ▼ ▼ ▼ ▼
For a smooth, frizz-free fringe, attach a nozzle to your dryer and direct hot air down the hair shafts to smooth down the cuticle. Style with a vent brush.

B·R·E·A·K·I·N·G THE CODE

Using the wrong conditioner can be just as bad as using none at all, so it's important to know what they do so you can choose the right one for you.

SURFACE CONDITIONERS

These smooth down the hair cuticles, remove tangles and leave a light, waxy residue. Like skin moisturisers, they leave a protective film on the hair shaft to prevent moisture escaping. Surface conditioners come in lotion, mousse, or leave-in spray formulas, and act in a matter of minutes. They are suitable for regular after-shampoo conditioning.

PENETRATIVE CONDITIONERS

These penetrate and moisturise deep within the hair shaft. They are designed to repair internal hair damage, and contain ingredients that moisturise and reinforce hair fibres. Penetrative conditioners are available as rich creams, mousses or leave-in restructurants. They are suitable for very dry hair.

COMBINATION CONDITIONERS

These treat both the surface hair cuticles and penetrate the hair shaft. Some types can be left on for just a few minutes, while others require 30 minutes processing time. They are available in lotion, cream or foam formulas, and are suitable for permed, coloured and heat damaged hair.

OIL TREATMENTS

These add shine, prevent hair strands drying out and reduce static. A concentrated shampoo, however, is needed to remove the oil, and this can counteract some of the benefit. Try hot oil conditioners as they are a light form of oil treatment and can be easily rinsed out. Some lotions have formulas that allow them to work selectively – they target dry areas without overloading healthy hair.

ALL-IN-ONE CONDITIONING SHAMPOOS

These are a recent development that can save time and money. Avoid them if your hair is very dry or if it's extra fine, as they can flatten your hair.

FOAMING CONDITIONERS

These have the same effect as conditioning lotions, but they penetrate every hair strand without having to be combed through. Simply spray on to damp hair and massage in.

Conditioning Mousse

Wash and towel dry your hair. Squirt a blob of mousse into your palm, massage it into your hair and comb it through to the ends.

89

HOT OIL TREATMENT

1 Fill a bowl with hot tap water and place the unopened tube of hot oil in the water. Leave the oil to heat up for about one minute.

2 Massage the hot oil into your hair shafts, and wrap your hair in a towel. Leave for five minutes, rinse and style as usual.

DRY ENDS REPAIR

Dry, split ends are a common problem, and although you can't mend split ends, regular conditioning keeps them looking their best before you have a chance to get them trimmed. While old-style conditioners, designed for dry end repair, were often heavy and sticky, today's colourless serums are lighter and have powerful conditioning properties. Dry end repair serum can be used on wet hair, or in between washes when ends feel dry.

1 Apply a few drops of the serum to wet hair after washing. Put the serum in the palm of your hand, and rub your palms together.

2 Massage the serum lightly into the hair ends to help absorption. Use a little more serum if the ends still feel dry after styling.

3 If you have layered hair, you may have dry ends near your crown. To reach them, smooth your palms over your head, then style as usual.

HAIR STYLING TECHNIQUE 17: DRY HAIR REPAIR

• PROJECT 16 •

MAKE YOUR OWN CONDITIONER

The next time you run out of conditioner, why not make your own with natural ingredients from the kitchen or garden? Project 16 shows you how to have healthy-looking hair, without resorting to salon treatments.

♥♥♥

Lifeless hair

1 avocado or 1 egg

Mash the avocado or beat the egg and apply to the hair. Leave on for 15-20 minutes, then rinse off with lukewarm water. Finally, shampoo and rinse your hair thoroughly.

tip Avocados and eggs are both messy, but will do wonders for the condition.

♥♥♥

Dry scalp

1 egg
1 tbsp vinegar
2 tbsp almond, olive or sunflower oil

Beat together the ingredients, then massage the mixture into your scalp and comb through to the ends of the hair. Leave for at least 15 minutes, then shampoo and rinse well.

♥♥♥

♥♥♥

Dull hair

1 egg
2 tbsp castor oil
1 tsp glycerine

Whisk together all the ingredients. Massage the mixture into your scalp and wrap your head in a hot towel to encourage absorption. Leave for at least 20 minutes, until the towel has cooled down. Then shampoo and rinse your hair thoroughly.

♥♥♥

Over-processed and heat-damaged hair

150ml (1/4 pt) olive, coconut, sesame or almond oil

Heat the oil to blood temperature. Apply to your scalp by parting your hair in sections, until the entire head is well covered. Comb through to distribute the oil to the ends of the hair, then massage into the scalp. Cover your hair in tin foil or a plastic cap, then wrap your head in a hot towel, so that the heat encourages absorption of the oil. Leave the treatment on at least until the towel has cooled down or, preferably, overnight. Wash out the oil using two applications of shampoo. Rinse thoroughly.

♥♥♥

91

♥ ♥ ♥
Flyaway hair

**4 tbsp fresh elderberries
water**

Crush the elderberries and strain the juice. Mix this with an equal quantity of water. Pour through the hair about five minutes before washing it. Then rinse out. Don't be put off by the smell – it won't linger for long.

♥ ♥ ♥
Hair loss

**100g (4oz) fresh mint, collected in two batches
225ml (8floz) almond oil**

Soak half the mint in the almond oil for two weeks. Strain through muslin and discard the mint. Repeat the process, using the same almond oil and another 50g (2oz) of fresh mint, and soak for another two weeks. Strain, and store in an airtight bottle. Massage the oil into the scalp regularly, and at least 30 minutes before washing the hair.

♥ ♥ ♥
Dandruff

**100g (4oz) fresh rosemary, collected in two batches
225ml (8floz) almond oil**

Prepare the oil as for Hair Loss, using fresh rosemary instead of mint. Massage into the scalp regularly, at least 30 minutes before washing out.

tip Using strong camomile tea as a final rinse also helps cure dandruff.

♥ ♥ ♥
Pick-me-up

**4 tsp fresh lemon juice
icy water**

Mix together and use as a final rinse.

tip Lemon gives the hair shine and keeps it looking glossy because it encourages the cuticle of the hair shafts to lie flat. Cider vinegar added to your final rinse has similar results.

TRICKS
– of the trade

If conditioner is not rinsed out properly, it can leave the hair looking dull and lank. Try one of these antidotes to refresh dulling tresses.

FOR FAIR HAIR:
**4 tbsp fresh camomile
or
2 tbsp dried camomile
600ml (1pt) boiling water**

FOR DARK HAIR:
**8 sprigs fresh rosemary
or
2 tbsp dried rosemary
600ml (1pt) boiling water**

Pour the boiling water over your chosen herb. Allow the water to cool, then strain.

Bend over a bowl and pour the infusion over your head. Catch the infusion in a second bowl as you pour. Carry on using the same infusion until your arm gets tired!

You can also use a herbal infusion as a relaxing massage tonic.

Rinse your hair in the tonic, then begin massaging your scalp with the palms of your hands. Lift up your hair at the neck, spread your fingers, and start working on the base of your scalp. Rotate your hands using small circular movements, exerting gentle pressure on the scalp. Make sure that the scalp moves and not just your hands!

Work your way slowly up the back of your head to the crown, kneading the scalp with rhythmic movements as you go. Gradually move out over the whole head, working firmly but gently into the hair line and surrounding area where tension builds up and traces of make-up tend to get trapped.

Then take the ends of your hair in your hands and rub in more tonic. When you have massaged the ends for at least 15-20 minutes, rinse your hair in warm water.

Suit yourself

Find out which herbs improve the condition of your hair, then rinse the infusion through your hair to add a lovely glossy shine.

TO MAKE AN INFUSION:
Add 2tbsp of fresh chopped herbs or 1tbsp of dried herbs to 600ml (1pt) boiling water in a glass container, then cover.

Leave the herbs to infuse for at least 15 minutes, but preferably longer, to strengthen the properties of the rinse. Strain, then pour the infusion over your hair using two containers – one to pour and the other to catch the infusion to use again.

ROSEMARY is good for reducing static in hair. Make a basic rosemary infusion and use it as a final rinse after shampooing. Or use between washes to help control unmanageable locks.

NETTLE helps to stimulate hair growth. Use a basic nettle infusion as a final rinse tonic. Luckily the stinging glands are destroyed by the boiling water!

PARSLEY helps prevent dandruff if you rub the infusion into your hair every two to three days. Use a double strength infusion for severe cases.